TapRooT®

Root Cause Tree® Dictionary

Seventh Edition

tap·root (tap´root´) ***n.*** [[TAP[2] + ROOT[1]]] 1) a main root, growing almost vertically downward, from which small branch roots spread out 2) the best way to find the root causes of accidents, incidents, equipment failures, quality issues, production problems, plant upsets, maintenance errors, or sentinel events

SYSTEM IMPROVEMENTS, INC.
238 South Peters Road, Suite 301
Knoxville, Tennessee 37923-5224
(865) 539-2139 fax: (865) 539-4335
website: www.taproot.com
e-mail: info@taproot.com

Library of Congress
Cataloging-in-Publication Data
Paradies, Mark / Unger, Linda
TapRooT® Root Cause Tree® Dictionary,
Seventh Edition
p. cm.
Definitions for use of the TaprooT® Root
Cause Tree®.
ISBN 978-1-893130-03-6
1. Business/Economics/Finance.
I. Paradies, Mark / Unger, Linda
II. Type – Non-Fiction.

PRINTED IN THE UNITED STATES OF AMERICA

TABLE OF CONTENTS

USING THE DICTIONARY

This pocket dictionary is for use with the Root Cause Tree®. It provides definitions for every category on the tree. The definitions are in the form of questions. That's why the Dictionary is sometimes called the Questionary. If you answer yes to a question, then that category applies to the causal factor or issue you are analyzing.

Also, the Dictionary is sometimes referred to as the "Debate Buster" because it helps settle debates between team members when using the Root Cause Tree®.

To simplify the text, instead of referring to causal factors or issues, we will call all problems "issues" in this dictionary.

To find a definition for a category on the tree, simply look for the name of the Basic Cause Category and Near Root Cause category in the block at the edge of each page or look in the Table of Contents.

The Root Cause Tree® is part of the TapRooT® System for root cause analysis and problem investigation. For details about the system or for detailed directions on how to use the tree, see the *TapRooT® Book*. To order the book, see:

www.taproot.com

or call System Improvements in the US at:

865-539-2139

NOTE: NI = Needs Improvement

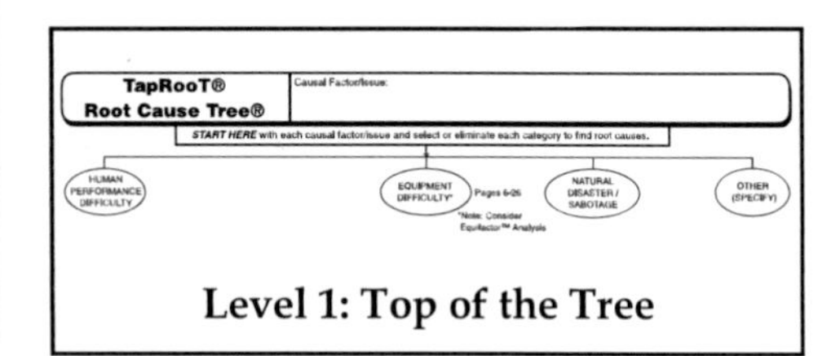

Level 1: Top of the Tree

HUMAN PERFORMANCE DIFFICULTY:

- Was the issue related to poor human performance?
- Was the issue caused by a:
  - simple mistake;
  - human error;
  - situational awareness issue; or
  - slip, lapse, or rule violation?
- Was the issue the result of:
  - work performed incorrectly;
  - work omitted or forgotten;
  - false assumptions;
  - broken rules;
  - incorrect calculations; or
  - other human actions that caused unwanted/unintended consequences?
- If a person had done something differently, would the issue have been prevented or significantly reduced?

- Was a mistake made because of poor design of the equipment, system, control, or display that led to a human error?

EQUIPMENT DIFFICULTY:

- Did the equipment break or wear out?
- Did the equipment fail due to:
  - a bad part?
  - a bad design?
  - no or poor preventive or predictive maintenance [PM]?
- Did software/code for the equipment fail?
- Did a failed component or other problem cause the control logic code/software to respond inappropriately?

NOTE: If the failure was caused by:
- improper operation;
- improper maintenance;
- installation errors;
- use for a purpose far beyond the intention of the design; or
- a design that causes a human performance difficulty

then the failure is ***NOT*** an *Equipment Difficulty*, but rather the failure is a *Human Performance Difficulty*. Therefore, the root causes should be investigated under the *Human Performance Difficulty* section of the Root Cause Tree®.

NOTE: If the information about this equipment failure is incomplete, troubleshoot the failure using Equifactor® Analysis. Information about Equifactor® Analysis can be found in the *TapRooT® Book*.

NATURAL DISASTER/SABOTAGE:

- Was the issue related to a:

- tornado	- hurricane	- earthquake
- flood	- mudslide	- blizzard
- ice storm	- avalanche	- lightning
- drought	- volcanic eruption	

- other natural disaster that could not be reasonably protected against by the facility's design?

(For example, protection could include using lightning rods to protect against lightning strikes in an area prone to thunderstorms.)

- Was the issue related to deliberate, harmful intentions, malicious actions intended to cause damage, intentional criminal acts, or acts of terrorism or violence intended to hurt people? (For example, a disturbed employee who destroys company property.)

NOTE: Horseplay or practical jokes, although intentional, usually are not intended to cause great harm or damage. Thus if the intention was not to cause harm or damage, horseplay or practical jokes should be investigated under *Human Performance Difficulty*.

OTHER:

- Was there insufficient detail to determine if the cause was a:
  - *Human Performance Difficulty,*
  - *Equipment Difficulty, or*
  - *Natural Disaster/Sabotage?*
- Was the issue not related to a topic covered by the other categories?

When you find an *Other*, record as much information about the cause as possible. Detail the efforts to identify a cause and the reasons that a specific cause on the tree could not be identified or the reasons why the other categories didn't apply.

Top of Tree

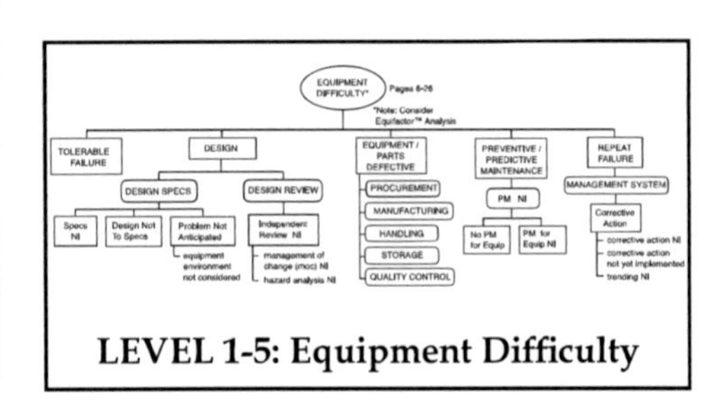

LEVEL 1-5: Equipment Difficulty

EQUIPMENT DIFFICULTY:

See the definition on page 3.

TOLERABLE
FAILURE

TOLERABLE FAILURE:

- Were the consequences of the failure minor?
- Would the cost of fixing the cause of this failure outweigh any potential benefits that preventing the failure might produce?
- Does the failure happen so infrequently and are the consequences small enough that developing corrective action is not worthwhile?

<u>NOTE</u>: Not all equipment failures are tolerable. This category is reserved for failures that are deemed to be acceptable (i.e., no corrective action is planned to prevent similar failures in the future). Therefore, if you decide this issue is a

Tolerable Failure, you should not identify causes for this issue anywhere else on the tree. Instead, record the failure so that it can be trended to identify *Repeat Failures.*

Do NOT use the *Tolerable Failure* category in the following specific instances:

1) Reasonable and sound PM practices for the equipment would have prevented failure. Refer to *PM.*
2) The failure is a repeat failure, & inadequate or no corrective action was taken to prevent recurrence. Refer to *corrective action NI.*
3) The failure is a repeat failure, and corrective action (for example: a design improvement) was identified but not implemented before recurrence. Refer to *corrective action not yet implemented.*
4) A sound and reasonable design or design review process would have prevented the failure. Refer to *Design.*
5) Sound quality control practices would have prevented the failure. Refer to *Quality Control* in the *Equipment/Parts Defective* category.
6) The failure was the result of a part that was defective when installed. Refer to *Equipment/Parts Defective.*
7) The failure was caused by human performance problems. Refer to *Human Performance Difficulty* at the top of the tree (Level 1).

DESIGN

DESIGN:

- Was the equipment and/or software/code designed in-house or did your engineers participate in the design and was the equipment difficulty due to a design problem that caused the equipment to fail?

NOTE: This category includes management of change and hazard analysis for equipment modifications.

NOTE: DO NOT use the *Design* section for human factors design issues. Human factors design issues cause human performance difficulties, so they should be analyzed under the *Human Performance Difficulty* category (at the top of the tree) NOT the *Equipment Difficulty* category.

NOTE: If the equipment was designed by the manufacturer without input from your engineers, you should analyze this issue under the *Equipment/Parts Defective* category under either the *Procurement* or *Manufacturing* categories.

NOTE: If a particular issue continues to recur because of design deficiencies, you should also investigate this issue under the *corrective action NI or corrective action not yet implemented* section of the tree.

DESIGN SPECS

DESIGN SPECS:
- Was an equipment malfunction or software/code problem caused by:
  - inadequate design specifications;
  - not designing the equipment or software/code to the specifications; or
  - not anticipating operational problems that should have been anticipated during the design process?

Specs NI

Specs NI:
- Was an equipment malfunction or software/code problem caused by incorrect or inadequate design specifications or basic data?
- Were appropriate design standards not used or incorrectly applied?
- Were the specifications incomplete?

Design Not To Specs

Design Not To Specs:
- Were the specifications for the design correct but the design did not meet the specifications?

NOTE: If the design review process should have caught the problem with the design not meeting the specifications, then consider analyzing the issue under the *Design Review* category as well as this category.

Problem Not Anticipated

Problem Not Anticipated:

- Did the designer not anticipate and design the equipment to withstand or adjust to potential problems that might occur during equipment service lifetime?
- Did the designer not anticipate and design the software/code for situations that should have been anticipated (for example, component failures or upset conditions)?

NOTE: If the design review process should have caught the issue with the equipment not being able to withstand or adjust to potential problems that might occur during equipment service lifetime, then you should investigate the design review process under the *Design Review* category of the tree.

NOTE: If the design review process should have caught the issue with the software/code not being able to accommodate potential problems due to component failures or plant upset conditions, then you should investigate the design review process under the *Design Review* category of the tree.

equipment environment not considered:

- Was a potential design problem not anticipated because the designer failed to consider the equipment environment?

Examples of failures that should be included in this category are:

1) Deterioration of gasket material in a diesel generator room due to exposure to diesel vapors; or
2) Failure of solenoid valves installed on outdoor boat davits due to exposure to the weather.

NOTE: If the design review process should have identified the equipment environment problems, then you should investigate the design review process under the *Design Review* category of the tree.

DESIGN REVIEW

DESIGN REVIEW:

- If this equipment or software/code was especially significant to safety, reliability, or quality:
  - Did the design review process fail to detect design errors that should have been detected?
  - Was the design review process inadequate?
  - Did an obvious error go undetected?
  - Was there no policy to perform a detailed review (management of

change) of design changes that could impact the facility's safety?
- Even though it was required, was management of change to an existing design not performed, or inadequately performed, when the design was altered?
- Was an analysis of the system's hazards not performed or not sufficient?

NOTE: Only select the *Design Review* category if the reviewer reasonably could have been expected to detect the error (realizing that the reviewer is usually not as familiar with a design as the designer).

Independent Review NI

Independent Review NI:

- Was the issue at least partially caused by inadequate independent review by someone other than the designer?
- Was there inadequate control of the independent review process to ensure that the correct people reviewed the design or design changes at the proper time during the design process?
- Was the management of change process not applied or improperly applied and, therefore, failed to detect problems created by a change?
- For the nuclear industry, was the 50.59 process improperly applied and, therefore, failed to detect unreviewed

safety questions or challenges to the facility's licensed design basis?

- Did the safety, environmental, or production significance of a design or a design change warrant an independent review of the design or design change and one was not performed or the review was somehow inadequate?
- Was an analysis of the system's hazards not performed or not sufficient?

NOTE: If you decide that an independent design review should have been required, you may want to investigate why the review was not performed. Since not performing the review is a human performance difficulty, you should use the *Human Performance Difficulty* section of the tree.

management of change (MOC) NI:

- Did the safety, environmental, or production significance of a design change warrant an independent review of the design change and one was not performed or the review was somehow inadequate?
- For industries covered by the OSHA Process Safety Management Regulation, the EPA's RMP, or other international process safety management regulations, was the management of change process not applied or improperly applied and, therefore, failed to detect hazards created by a change?

- For the nuclear industry, was the 50.59 process improperly applied and, therefore, failed to detect unreviewed safety questions or challenges to the facility's licensed design basis?

NOTE: If you decide that a management of change should have been required or should have been performed more thoroughly, you may want to investigate why the MOC was not performed or why it was not performed more thoroughly. Since these issues are human performance difficulties, you should use the *Human Performance Difficulty* section of the tree for this analysis.

hazard analysis NI:

- Did the safety, environmental, or production significance of a process warrant an independent analysis of the process's hazards, but the hazard analysis was not performed or not sufficient to detect hazards that should have been recognized and corrected?

NOTE: If you decide that a hazard analysis should have been required or should have been performed more thoroughly, you may want to investigate why the hazard analysis was not performed or why it was not performed more thoroughly. Since these issues are human performance difficulties, you should use the *Human Performance Difficulty* section of the tree for this analysis.

EQUIPMENT / PARTS DEFECTIVE

EQUIPMENT/PARTS DEFECTIVE:

- Was a part defective before it was installed?
- Were parts or equipment proven to be defective because they were manufactured improperly, procured improperly, handled improperly during shipping (including packaging problems), stored improperly, or received inadequate quality checks before being installed?
- Was software/code defective or inappropriate for the system?
- Were operational quality checks of software/code performance inadequate?

NOTE: If the part was broken during installation due to a human error, then the issue should be analyzed as a *Human Performance Difficulty* rather than an *Equipment Difficulty*.

NOTE: If software/code caused a human error, then the issue should be analyzed as a *Human Performance Difficulty* rather than an *Equipment Difficulty*.

PROCUREMENT

PROCUREMENT:

- Were defective or improper parts or equipment obtained from a vendor because

of problems in the procurement process?
- Was software/code inadequate for the system because of problems in the procurement process?

NOTE: If one needs to find the root cause(s) of the procurement problem, the investigator will have to develop a new SnapCharT® for the procurement of the defective part or software/code and then identify the issue(s)/ causal factor(s) that need further analysis to discover the procurement problem's root cause(s).

MANUFACTURING

MANUFACTURING:
- Were defective or improper parts or equipment delivered by a vendor as a result of manufacturing problems?
- Was software/code with obvious malfunctions or "bugs" provided by software vendors?

NOTE: If one needs to find the root cause(s) of the manufacturing problem that led to the production of a defective part or software/code, then the investigator will have to develop a new SnapCharT® of the manufacturing or software development process that led up to the production of the defective part or software/code. If the part or software/ code was produced by an outside vendor/manufacturer, this means expanding the investigation to their facility and processes.

HANDLING

HANDLING:

- Were parts, equipment, or software media damaged during handling before installation?

NOTE: If one needs to find the root cause(s) of the handling problem, the investigator will have to develop a new SnapCharT® for the handling of the defective item and then analyze each issue to find its root cause(s).

NOTE: This does not include items that were damaged during the installation process due to human performance difficulties (for example, a mechanic applying excessive force). Human performance issues during installation should be analyzed as a *Human Performance Difficulty* rather than an *Equipment Difficulty*.

STORAGE

STORAGE:

- Were parts, equipment or software media damaged during storage before installation?
- Was an item past its storage shelf life?

NOTE: If one needs to find the root cause(s) of the storage problem, the investigator will have to develop a new SnapCharT® for the storage problem and then analyze each issue to find its root cause(s).

QUALITY CONTROL

QUALITY CONTROL:

For definitions see pages 71-77.

PREVENTIVE / PREDICTIVE MAINTENANCE

PREVENTIVE / PREDICTIVE MAINTENANCE:

- Should a reasonable Preventive or Predictive Maintenance (PM) program have prevented the equipment, software difficulty or malfunction?
- Was there no PM for the equipment or was the PM inadequate?
- If this equipment was especially significant to safety, reliability, or quality, should a Risk Based Inspection (RBI) Program have been in place to catch and prevent (or reduce the likelihood of) the equipment failure?
- If this equipment was especially significant to safety, reliability, or quality, should a Reliability Centered Maintenance (RCM) Program or other maintenance analysis program have been in place to prevent or reduce the likelihood of the equipment failure?

NOTE: Use this category only if a sound PM (based on the significance of the equipment to safety and production, industry/operating experience and vendor recommendations, or a RCM Program) is not being performed. It is not reasonable to expect PM to prevent all malfunctions or to expect extensive PM to be performed on every piece of equipment.

NOTE: If a PM, RCM, or RBI Program existed and it was not used, then this is a *Human Performance Difficulty* and you should consider analyzing the failure to use the program under the *Human Performance Difficulty* category.

PM NI

PM NI:

- Was a malfunction caused by the lack of a Preventive or Predictive Maintenance (PM) Program, Reliability Centered Maintenance (RCM) Program, or Risk Based Inspection (RBI) Program?
- Was a failure caused by an inadequate PM/RCM/RBI Program?
- Should an adequate PM/RCM/RBI Program have detected and prevented, or reduced the likelihood of the malfunction?
- Did industry experience indicate that the equipment needed routine PM/RCM/RBI and that program wasn't provided?

<u>NOTE</u>: Only use this category if a sound, reasonable PM/RCM/RBI Program is not being performed for a piece of equipment based on industry or operating experience or vendor recommendations. Do not expect PM/RCM/RBI to prevent all malfunctions or expect extensive PM, RCM, RBIs to be performed on every piece of equipment.

<u>NOTE</u>: If a PM/RCM/RBI program existed and it was not used (resulting in no PM or no inspection), consider analyzing the failure to use the program under the *Human Performance Difficulty* category.

No PM for Equip

No PM for Equip:

- Was a malfunction caused by a lack of preventive or predictive maintenance (PM) Program, Reliability Centered Maintenance (RCM) Program, or Risk Based Inspection (RBI) Program for the equipment or software/code?
- Was a malfunction caused by having no PM scheduled for a piece of equipment/software code?
- Should there have been PM for the particular equipment/component that failed or software/code that malfunctioned?
- Did the vendor recommend performing any PM on the equipment/software code that should have prevented this malfunction but it was not

being performed because it was not scheduled?

- Did operating or industry experiences indicate that the equipment needed routine PM/RCM/RBI to prevent failure but it was not being performed?

NOTE: If a PM/RCM/RBI program existed and it was not used (resulting in no PM or RBI), analyze the failure to use the program under the *Human Performance Difficulty* category.

PM for Equip NI

PM for Equip NI:

- Was preventive or predictive maintenance (PM) or Risk Based Inspections (RBI) scheduled too infrequently, considering the vendor recommendations and operating experience for the equipment?
- Was PM/RBI being performed on some components of the equipment or system but no PM/RBI was being performed on other components that needed PM/RBI?
- Was PM/RBI being performed but better PM/RBI was available and wasn't being used when it should have been used?

REPEAT FAILURE

REPEAT FAILURE:

- Was the equipment/software code difficulty:

1) Known to have occurred in the past; and
2) Did previous failures occur frequently enough that they should have been recognized as repetitive; and
3) Was there enough time since the failure that it should have been recognized as repetitive so that management should have implemented interim compensatory actions or effective corrective action to prevent recurrence of the problem?

NOTE: If an equipment difficulty is recorded under this category, another cause under *PM, Design,* or *Equipment/ Parts Defective* should also be found because some issue is continuing to cause the equipment/software code to fail.

MANAGEMENT SYSTEM

MANAGEMENT SYSTEM:

- Was an issue caused by failure to provide corrective action for known deficiencies (recurring failures) or by implementing inadequate corrective action?
- Was the corrective action that could have prevented the issue proposed, but not implemented in a reasonable time, before the issue recurred?
- Was there a failure to implement effective interim compensatory actions while waiting to implement final corrective actions?

- Would better trending of problems have led to the discovery of a generic (systemic) issue that, if corrected, could have prevented this issue?

Corrective Action

Corrective Action:

- Was an issue caused by failure to provide corrective action for known equipment/ software/code malfunctions, unreliable equipment, or equipment deficiencies?
- Was an issue caused by implementing inadequate corrective action?
- Was the corrective action that would have prevented the issue proposed, but not implemented in a reasonable time, before the issue recurred?
- If implementation of permanent, effective corrective actions was delayed due to budget, equipment/software code availability, or other considerations, should there have been some type of interim compensatory actions in place to prevent or reduce the likelihood of the equipment/software code malfunction?
- Would better trending of equipment problems have led to the discovery of a generic (systemic) issue that, if corrected, could have prevented this failure?

NOTE: In this section, known deficiencies are any deficiencies that had previously been identified to supervision or management and sufficient time had passed so that effective corrective action should have been implemented. One should maintain a list of specific recurring failures to improve the consistency of root cause analysis in this category.

NOTE: If an investigator finds a *Corrective Action* near root cause, then it is important for the investigator to find out what caused the original failure. Both of these causes (the *Corrective Action* cause and the original cause of the failure) should be recorded and corrected. The original cause could be a *PM, Design,* or *Equipment/Parts Defective* issue.

corrective action NI:

- Was an issue caused by failure to provide corrective action for known deficiencies (recurring failures)?
- Was a corrective action for a known deficiency not recommended?
- Was a corrective action for a known deficiency disregarded?
- Did the corrective action address only the symptoms of a problem and fail to address the root causes?
- Did management decide to implement lower cost or otherwise different corrective actions that didn't adequately fix the previously discovered issue?
- Was an implemented interim compensatory action or corrective action unsuccessful in preventing an issue's recurrence?

- Should the failure of a corrective action have been detected by a corrective action effectiveness review (validation) but it was not checked?

corrective action not yet implemented:

- Was a corrective action that would have prevented the issue proposed, but not implemented in a reasonable time, before the issue recurred? (Reasons for failure to implement a corrective action may include delays in funding, delays in project design, abnormal length of the corrective action to implementation cycle, or lack of emphasis on the implementation of corrective actions.)
- Did failure to track the implementation of corrective actions lead to unacceptable delays in the implementation of corrective actions or failure to implement corrective actions that were recommended and approved?
- Was there a failure to implement effective interim compensatory actions while waiting to implement final corrective actions?

<u>NOTE</u>: One must allow a reasonable time for implementation of corrective actions. The time allowed should be based on the seriousness of the issue and the scope of the work required to correct it. However, adequate interim compensatory actions should be taken while awaiting the final corrective actions. This action could include

not restarting the plant or process until management judges that it is safe to do so.

trending NI:

- Would better trending of failures and root causes have led to the discovery of a generic (systemic) problem that, if corrected, should have prevented this issue?
- Was a significant trend that indicated a problem missed because the facility didn't use proper statistical process control trending techniques?

NOTE: If a trend was detected but adequate interim compensatory actions or corrective actions were not proposed, the root cause should be recorded under corrective action NI.

NOTE: If a trend was detected but adequate interim compensatory actions or corrective actions were proposed but were not implemented in a timely manner, the root cause should be recorded under *corrective action not yet implemented.*

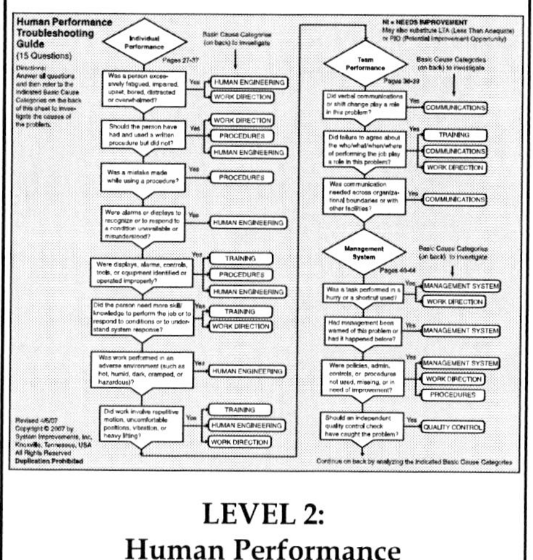

LEVEL 2:
Human Performance
Troubleshooting Guide
(15 Questions)

Individual Performance

Was a person excessively fatigued, impaired, upset, bored, distracted or overwhelmed?

1. Was a person excessively fatigued, impaired, upset, bored, distracted, or overwhelmed? This question focuses on factors that can reduce human reliability and cause human errors.

- For substance abuse, fatigue, or personal problems, could a properly trained supervisor detect the aberrant behavior and, therefore, the supervisor should not have assigned the worker to the job (or should have taken steps to keep the worker out of harm's way)?

NOTE: Personal problems are problems that distract a person from the work being performed so that his or her performance is unreliable.

- When evaluating fatigue, was the worker "excessively" fatigued so that the supervisor should have detected the worker's excessive fatigue and taken action such as assigning someone else to perform the work? (This fatigue might be caused by excessive overtime, sleep disorders, or personal circumstances.)
- Was shift scheduling such that it caused people to be excessively fatigued?
- Do the hours assigned to a worker violate laws or industry standards?
- Was more than 16 hours worked in a row?
- Did the person report being fatigued?
- Did the person have a sleep disorder?
- Was the person called in 8 or more hours early to start work?
- Was the person sleep deprived? (Had his or her normal sleep been significantly disrupted?)

- Did the person exhibit periods of "microsleep" prior to the problem? (Microsleep is brief intrusions of sleep typically repeated at 5-15 second intervals with slow eye rolling movements, repeated eye closures, head bobbing, and mental incapacitation).
- Did the person exhibit "Automatic Behavior Syndrome"? (Intrusions of sleep characterized by eyes wide open in a blank, fixed, unfocused gaze, and mental incapacitation.)

The bored or distracted part of the question goes beyond alertness problems caused by substance abuse or fatigue. It includes attention problems caused by jobs that are poorly designed and, therefore, cause extreme boredom and failure to detect problems.

- Was this job designed so that the average worker normally or frequently becomes bored and stops monitoring key indicators?
- Was the work so uninteresting that the person was easily distracted and missed key indications?

The overwhelmed part of this question focuses on the workload the individual faced.

- Were there so many alarms or signals that the person could not see or interpret them?
- Was the person overloaded with work?

- Did the person miss key signals because s/he was too busy to see them?
- Was the person reacting as fast as possible but still unable to keep up with the pace of new signals, control actions, or other required responses?
- Was there a crisis that overwhelmed the senses or the person's ability to respond?

NOTE: This question does not include conscious decisions by a worker to ignore indications or a procedure's requirements. It also does not include horseplay or other violations of company rules. These types of problems will be analyzed in later questions.

Should the person have had and used a written procedure but did not?

2. Should the person have had and used a written procedure but did not? This question has to do with difficulties caused by the person performing the work not using a written procedure or intentionally deviating from the written procedure. To answer this question, one has to understand the definition of a procedure as used in the Root Cause Tree®. Therefore, we will define how we use the term here and then provide guidance for the analyst to help them determine when they should answer "Yes" to this question.

<u>**Definition of "Procedure" in the Root Cause Tree®:**</u> A "procedure" is a written step-by-step description of how a particular task is to be performed that is ***read and followed during performance of the work*** by the person performing the work (or by two people doing the work - one reading and one doing). Examples of procedures include: equipment start-up or shutdown procedures, normal operating procedures, written operating instructions, pre-flight checklists, abnormal operating procedures, emergency procedures, maintenance procedures, special test procedures, preventive maintenance procedures, construction installation procedures, calibration procedures, hydrostatic test procedures, and inspection procedures.

We do NOT include in this definition "administrative procedures" that are only used as a reference and are not actively referred to while the work is being performed. These types of administrative procedures usually are NOT written in a step-by-step format and are NOT referred to after initial training. Examples of administrative procedures that are NOT included in this definition of a procedure include: safety manuals, work practice guides, programming guides, training manuals, employment manuals, company policy manuals, management directives, and vision statements. These types of administrative controls are considered in the management section of the guide and are included in the *Management System* section of the Root Cause Tree®.

We do NOT include in this definition "ways of conducting work" that ***aren't written*** but rather are learned in training. Examples of these learned methods for performing work are: 1) a hospital "procedure" for an appendectomy; 2) the "procedure" for starting your car; or 3) "skill of the craft" knowledge of how to use a screwdriver. If the task is a memorized way of doing something, rather than a written checklist, then we would NOT call the practice a "procedure" for the use of this guide. Problems performing this type of work are analyzed under the Training section of the Root Cause Tree®.

So when should you answer "Yes" to this question? If the person performing the work failed to use a procedure because:

- There was no procedure.
- There was no clear prompt or cue to use the procedure.
- The person missed or didn't understand the prompt or cue to use the procedure.
- The supervisor should have, but didn't, mention the procedure in the pre-job brief.

- The procedure wasn't noted in the work package being used.
- There was no requirement to use the procedure.
- The person forgot to use the procedure.
- There was a conscious decision not to use the procedure or to skip a step or steps.
- The person started using the procedure but then made a conscious decision to deviate from what the procedure said to do.
- The person tried to perform the steps from memory and remembered incorrectly or omitted a step.

Was a mistake made while using a procedure?

3. Was a mistake made while using a procedure? This question covers errors made when following a procedure as written (see prior definition of "procedure" on page 31). In TapRooT® terminology, using a procedure means reading it and doing what is written (as pilots do when performing a pre-flight checklist).

- Was the procedure followed incorrectly?
- Did the person try to follow a procedure but still made a mistake?

- Was the wrong procedure used?
- Was the procedure followed as it was written but following it still caused a difficulty?
- Did the procedure leave out critical information or not cover all situations that should have been reasonably anticipated?
- Did the way the procedure was written cause confusion, a misunderstanding, or a mistake?

Were alarms or displays to recognize or to respond to a condition unavailable or misunderstood?

4. Were alarms or displays to recognize or to respond to a condition unavailable or misunderstood? This question focuses on the human-machine interface that was needed to recognize conditions or problems and understand what was occurring.

- Was the information provided by alarms or displays insufficient?
- Was the information needed to analyze or respond to a condition unclear?
- Was the person so overwhelmed by excessive information that important information wasn't detected among the clutter?
- Was the panel, computer screen, or workspace layout such that important

information was obstructed?
- Was an alarm/display not seen or heard?
- Was an alarm/display misunderstood?

Were displays, alarms, controls, tools, or equipment identified or operated improperly?

5. Were displays, alarms, controls, tools, or equipment identified or operated improperly? This question covers actual task performance.

- Was the device, equipment, or control operated or set up improperly?
- Was it operated according to the procedure but still caused a problem?
- Was a display or alarm misidentified and, therefore, the action taken was wrong?
- Was the person confused because of similarities between equipment, tools, or controls that were not identical?
- Was the tool specified to perform a job not the correct one?
- Was the wrong tool, device, equipment, or control used?
- Were the equipment, tools, controls, displays, or alarms so complicated that the person didn't use them properly?
- Was a simple error made in the use or set up of a tool, a control, or the equipment?

6. Did the person need more skill/ knowledge to perform the job or to respond to conditions or to understand system response? This question focuses on the knowledge, skills, and abilities of the person performing the task.

- Was the person not qualified to perform the task?
- Did the person fail to attend required training?
- Would better training have provided the person with the skill or knowledge required to correctly perform the task?
- Did the person understand what was to be done but didn't have the necessary skill to perform the task?
- Did the person forget what was required to be done because either the initial training didn't emphasize it enough or because the task was performed infrequently and continuing training wasn't provided?
- Did the supervisor fail to mention possible problems that should have been discussed and actions to take in the pre-job brief?
- Was the job performed infrequently, and should the supervisor have walked through the task with the person assigned to perform the work?

Was work performed in an adverse environment (such as hot, humid, dark, cramped, or hazardous)?

7. Was work performed in an adverse environment (such as hot, humid, dark, cramped, or hazardous)? This question focuses on environmental factors that can degrade human performance.

- Did the environmental conditions increase the risk associated with the job?
- Did the environmental conditions make the task more difficult?
- Did the person rush to get the work done because of the environmental conditions? (For example, it was very cold so s/he hurried to get the work done to return to a heated part of the facility.)
- Did the person have trouble seeing or hearing?
- Was there too little room to use tools or perform the work?
- Was the housekeeping so poor that it caused mistakes or personnel hazards?
- Were inadequate safeguards used to minimize or mitigate hazardous environmental conditions?

Did work involve repetitive motion, uncomfortable positions, vibration, or heavy lifting?

8. Did work involve repetitive motion, uncomfortable positions, vibration, or heavy lifting? This question focuses on the ergonomics of the task performance.

- Was the issue related to an overuse injury of the musculoskeletal system (for example, a back injury, a sprained knee, or carpal tunnel syndrome)?
- Could the issue have been prevented by better ergonomic design?

Team Performance

Did verbal communications or shift change play a role in this problem?

9. Did verbal communications or shift change play a role in this problem? This question is meant to detect communication issues.

- Was communication involved as part of the issue?
- Did a shift change or work turnover occur during the issue being analyzed?

Did failure to agree about the who/what/when/where of performing the job play a role in this problem?

10. Did failure to agree about the who/what/when/where of performing the job play a role in this problem? This question focuses on the verbal communications during preparation and coordination of the people performing the task.

- Did the people actively involved in the task fail to agree on what was to be done, who was to do it, when and where it was to be accomplished?
- During verbal communications, did someone misunderstand what was to be done or how it was to be accomplished?
- Was there disagreement about verbal instructions?
- Did someone misunderstand or fail to see or hear verbal or other forms of communications?
- Was incorrect action taken based on something that someone thought they heard?
- Did someone fail to act because they didn't hear something?
- Did someone act on his or her own when teamwork was required to successfully perform the task?

Was communication needed across organizational boundaries or with other facilities?

11. Was communication needed across organizational boundaries or with other facilities? This question focuses on communication outside the team performing the work.

- Was communication needed from one organization to another (for example, from hospital admitting to a treating physician)?
- Was there a misunderstanding that occurred because communication from one organization to another did not occur?
- Did a facility have to arrange for services from another facility or company?
- Did communication break down between organizations?

Management System

Was a task performed in a hurry or a shortcut used?

12. Was a task performed in a hurry or a shortcut used? This question is used to identify times when rules, policies, procedures, or administrative controls were bypassed and thereby caused a problem.

- Was there unusual pressure to complete the job?
- Were policies not followed?
- Were procedures disregarded?
- Did someone violate a rule or standard?
- Did rushing to get a job complete lead to shortcuts?
- To get the job done quickly, was a shortcut taken in the planning, preparation, or obtaining a work permit?
- Should more time or more people have been scheduled to perform this task to reduce the workload and potential for errors?

Had management been warned of this problem or had it happened before?

13. Had management been warned of this problem or had it happened before? This question focuses on management's ability to prevent the problem by taking timely action to previously recognized issues. Only issues related directly to the Causal Factor being considered should be analyzed here.

- Did this issue happen before and corrective action should have been in place to prevent it from happening again?

- Did this issue happen before, and the corrective actions taken were ineffective in preventing the issue's recurrence?
- Were corrective actions for this type of issue backlogged because of funding or other resource shortages?
- Was management specifically informed of the risk of this issue but chose to work without additional safeguards?
- Was the issue detected by an audit but no, or ineffective, corrective action was taken?
- Was this a frequent issue that management never heard about, so no corrective action was taken?
- Should a program to look for trends have identified the issue because of its repetitive nature?
- Did employee complaints about the issue fail to reach the appropriate level so that corrective actions could be taken?

Were policies, admin. controls, or procedures not used, missing, or in need of improvement?

14. Were policies, admin. controls, or procedures not used, missing, or in need of improvement? This question focuses on the completeness, usefulness, and use of policies, administrative controls, standards, and procedures.

- Were procedures or policies not fully complied with?
- Were policies creatively misinterpreted?
- Should there have been a policy or procedure to prevent this problem (for example, other similar facilities have a policy or procedure for this type of work) but there wasn't one?
- Did the policy need to be improved?
- Did the facility's policies and procedures fail to meet government, industry, and corporate standards?
- Was a required policy or procedure not used?
- Was a required policy or procedure consciously violated or deviated from?
- Should there have been a requirement for an effective audit program to detect this kind of problem?

Should an independent quality control check have caught the problem?

15. Should an independent quality control check have caught the problem? This question focuses on the formal quality inspection program for hazardous or high consequence work. This question does not apply to self-checking. To answer "Yes" to this question you must determine that an independent - completely separate - quality check should be performed prior to proceeding to the next step in the process/procedure/job.

- Should this task have required an independent quality inspection (QC hold point and inspection) before proceeding to the next step?
- Was an independent check (inspection) performed that didn't catch the problem?

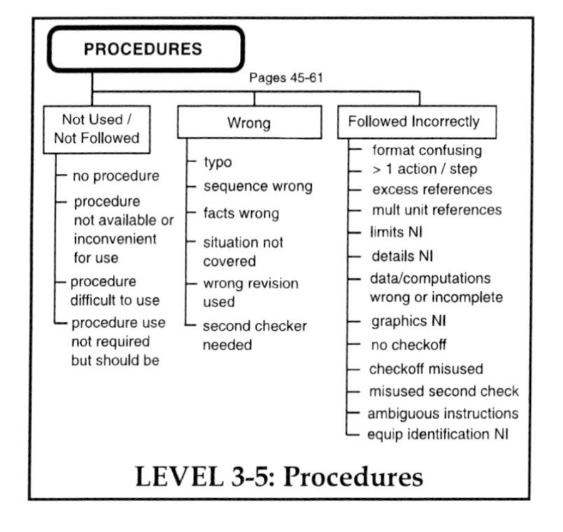

LEVEL 3-5: Procedures

Procedures

PROCEDURES

PROCEDURES:
The first question to ask is:

Would performance improve if a well written procedure was used correctly?

If the answer is yes, then you should continue to analyze this category. Depending on the type of task, procedures can help people perform more reliably. However, not all tasks are improved by procedures. Therefore, before analyzing this Basic Cause Category, a person must decide if using a procedure would improve human performance. If the answer is yes, continue to analyze the *Procedures* Basic Cause Category.

Some other questions that may indicate that you should be analyzing the *Procedures* category are:

- Was a procedure for the work not being used when it should have been?
- Would performance improve if the work was NOT being performed from memory (but rather, by using a checklist)?
- Was a procedure consciously not followed (deviated from)?
- Was a procedure followed incorrectly?
- Was a mistake made while trying to follow a procedure?
- Was a procedure wrong?
- Should the task have been performed by use of a procedure but there wasn't one to use?

NOTE: Not all problems or user unfriendly designs can be expected to be overcome by providing detailed procedures to "work-around" user unfriendly designs. Therefore, DO NOT record the cause as *Procedures - Followed Incorrectly* if better human factors design would have prevented the issue. Instead, analyze the cause under *Human Engineering*.

NOTE: Analyze the cause under *Training* if reasonable amounts of additional training are needed to ensure personnel successfully accomplish the work when using a procedure.

NOTE: To analyze procedure causes, people must agree on: "What is a procedure?" In the TapRooT® System, we have defined "procedure" as follows:

Definition of "Procedure" in the Root Cause Tree®: A "procedure" is a written step-by-step description of how a particular task is to be performed that is ***read and followed during performance of the work*** by the person performing the work (or by two people doing the work - one reading and one doing). Examples of procedures include: equipment start-up or shutdown procedures, normal operating procedures, written operating instructions, pre-flight checklists, abnormal operating procedures, emergency procedures, maintenance procedures, special test procedures, preventive maintenance procedures, construction installation procedures, calibration procedures, hydrostatic test procedures, and inspection procedures.

We do NOT include in this definition "administrative procedures" that are only used as a reference and are not actively referred to while the work is being performed. These types of administrative procedures usually are NOT written in a step-by-step format and are NOT referred to after initial training. Examples of administrative procedures that are NOT included in this definition of a procedure are: safety manuals, work practice guides, programming guides, training manuals, employment manuals, company policy manuals, management directives, and vision statements. These types of administrative controls are considered in the management section of the guide and are included in the *Management System* section of the Root Cause Tree®.

We do NOT include in this definition "ways of conducting work" that ***aren't written*** but rather are learned in training. Examples of these learned methods for performing work are: 1) a hospital "procedure" for an appendectomy; 2) the "procedure" for starting your car; or 3) "skill of the craft" knowledge of how to use a screwdriver. If the task is a memorized way of doing something, rather than a written checklist, then we would NOT call the practice a "procedure" for the use of this guide. Problems performing this type of work are analyzed under the *Training* section of the Root Cause Tree®.

Not Used / Not Followed

Not Used/Not Followed:

- Was the task done without a procedure when one should have been used?

- Would performance improve if the work was NOT being performed from memory but rather, by using a checklist?
- Was there no procedure for the work, but this type of work should have had a procedure?
- Did the person consciously decide not to use the procedure?
- Did the person consciously decide to do something different from what the procedure said to do?

NOTE: If a procedure was available and was required to be used but was not used or was consciously not followed or deviated from, you should also consider looking for causes under the *Management System - SPAC Not Used* section of the Root Cause Tree®. Or, if the procedure was consciously not followed, and the management system allowed deviation from the procedure without adequate review and approval, consider looking for causes under the *Management System - SPAC NI* section of the Root Cause Tree®.

no procedure:

- Was there no procedure for the job, but a procedure should have been available?

Depending on the type of task, procedures can help people perform more reliably.

However, not all tasks are improved by procedures.
Therefore, before selecting this root cause you must decide if using a procedure would improve human performance of the issue being analyzed. Some tasks that should probably have procedures include tasks that could result in unacceptable consequences if not performed exactly right (for example, failure to set the flaps during takeoff in an airplane), tasks that require documentation (for example, assembly of nuclear fuel), tasks that require considerable amounts of short term memory (for example, performing a valve line-up of 50 valves), tasks that are performed infrequently (for example, plant start-ups that are performed annually), and tasks that are performed under stress or with frequent interruptions (for example, emergency response procedures for a plant upset).

procedure not available or inconvenient for use:

- Was a procedure not handy for use? (There may have been no copy of the procedure in the work area, or perhaps there was only one master copy that had to be reproduced before use.)
- Was a procedure inconvenient to use? (Some working conditions or locations such as tight quarters, contamination

zones, or protective clothing make handling procedures inconvenient.)

NOTE: This root cause does not include the work being inconvenient to perform.

procedure difficult to use:

- Did the personnel performing the job consider the procedure too difficult to use and, therefore, decided not to use it?

Examples of procedures that are too difficult to use include procedures that are cumbersome, can't be understood, are impossible to perform as written, or are wrong or sequenced poorly so that the worker invented a different (inappropriate) way to perform the work.

NOTE: Consider the training that personnel should have had for this job. If better training would have made the procedure easier to use, then consider looking for root causes under the *Training* section of the Root Cause Tree®.

NOTE: Consider the preparation for the job. If this type of job was infrequent or complex and if a better pre-job brief or walk-thru by a supervisor would have made the procedure easier to use, consider looking for root causes under the *Work Direction* section of the Root Cause Tree®.

procedure use not required but should be: The question focuses on procedures that are used as references but should be in hand and used more as a checklist every time the work is performed.

- If a procedure exists but it is not required to be used, should its use be required because of the significance of the job or for other reasons?
- Was a procedure available but consciously not followed because the policy allowed deviation from the procedure without adequate review and approval?

<u>NOTE</u>: If there is no policy about using procedures and you think there should be a policy, look for root causes under the *Management System - Standards, Policies, or Administrative Controls NI* section of the Root Cause Tree®.

<u>NOTE</u>: If the policy allowed deviation from the procedure without adequate review & approval, consider looking for root causes under the *Management System - Standards, Policies, or Administrative Controls NI* section of the Root Cause Tree®.

Wrong

Wrong:
Was the procedure used and:

- Was the procedure factually wrong?
- Did it fail to address a situation

that reasonably should have been expected to occur while performing the procedure?

- Was the wrong revision of the procedure used?
- Because of the risk involved, should the procedure have required a second check of some action, but it did not?

typo:

- Was a typographical error in the procedure responsible for the issue?

sequence wrong:

- Were tasks and action steps not sequenced according to technical necessity and physical layout of equipment involved (even though the correct information was present)?

facts wrong:

- Were the steps in the procedure factually incorrect (for example: improper instructions, numerical values, wrong names or numbers for equipment, or improper equipment set-up instructions)?

situation not covered:

- Did the procedure fail to address all situations that reasonably should have been expected to occur during completion of the procedure? (For example, a start-up procedure may require actions that if not taken at just the right time, may lead to failure of indications that could mislead the operator.)

wrong revision used:

- Was the wrong revision of a procedure being used? (The wrong revision may be used for a variety of reasons, such as delays in printing and placing approved revisions in the field, failure to discard old revisions when new ones are issued, or failure to enter approved temporary procedure changes.)

second checker needed:

A second checker is an additional, trained individual that independently and formally reviews work to verify that it was completed correctly.

- Was the procedure significant enough to require a second checker to verify that the objective of a task or series of actions has been achieved, but a second checker wasn't required and provided for in the procedure?

NOTE: If there is no policy requiring a second checker for procedures that have significant safety or production loss risks, consider the root cause of *no SPAC under Management System – Standards, Policies, or Administrative Controls NI.*

Followed Incorrectly:

NOTE: This near-root cause *"Followed Incorrectly"* is for use when people were trying to follow a procedure but made a mistake and did not do what the procedure writer intended, perhaps because the procedure was somehow difficult to follow. You should NOT use this near-root cause if the person:

- Consciously deviates from the procedure,
- Did not have the procedure to follow, or
- Was using the procedure from memory.

In these cases, consider the root causes under the *Procedures* near-root cause category *not used/not followed:*

- Did the person performing the task try to use the procedure as written but still made a mistake?
- Was the issue related to following a procedure incorrectly?
- Was a second check missed?

NOTE: If the cause for incorrectly following the procedure cannot be found in one of the root causes under *Followed Incorrectly,* consider the other Basic Cause Categories recommended by the Human Performance Troubleshooting Guide (especially *Human Engineering and Training*).

Procedures (Followed Incorrectly)

format confusing:

- Was the layout or format of the procedure such that it could not be easily, rapidly, and precisely read and understood?
- Did the arrangement (e.g., use of indentation, logical grouping) of the action steps and its supporting information reduce comprehension?
- Does the layout of the procedure fail to conform to the facility's guidance concerning organization into sections (e.g., objective, initial conditions, immediate actions, subsequent actions, diagnostic aids)?
- Are notes, warnings, and caution notices inaccurate or too wordy?
- Do notes, warnings, and caution notices contain action steps?
- Was the procedure written at too high a grade level so that the procedure was confusing and could not be reliably used by those performing the work?
- Was the vocabulary used not sufficiently simple, familiar, and specific to accurately convey the intended meaning?
- Were the abbreviations, acronyms, and symbols used unfamiliar to the user?
- Are the instructions in the procedure unclear because of poor sentence structure or punctuation?
- Are "IF ... THEN ..." instructions, conditional statements, or logic sequences confusing?

> 1 action per step:

- Did the procedure step have more than one action which lead to an action being skipped?
- Was a step written in paragraph format rather than in crisp, single action statements and this led to an action being skipped?

excess references:

- Did the procedure refer to too many other procedures causing the person using the procedure to become confused, lose his or her place, or omit steps in one of the multiple procedures?

multiple unit references:

- Was there confusion or errors because the procedure contained references to multiple plants or units? [For example: the procedure states, "Stop pump if level reaches 65 inches (40 in. at Unit 2)" but the pump was not stopped at 40 inches in Unit 2 because they only read the 65 inches limit that applied to Unit 1.]

limits NI:

- Were limits or permissible operating ranges not expressed in absolute numbers but instead expressed in a "+ or -" format? (For example, expressing the limits as "1.39 ± 0.69" is much more likely to cause errors than using "0.70 to 2.08".)

Procedures (Followed Incorrectly)

details NI:

- Was the procedure written at an inappropriate level of technical detail given the training and experience required for personnel performing the work?
- Did a step in the procedure state one action but require several unwritten steps to be completed from memory? (For example, "replace the pump" is one action that may require many implicit steps, including tagging out the pump, disconnecting fluid lines and electrical power.)

data/computations wrong or incomplete:

- Was an error made because of a mistake in recording or transferring data or because of incorrect calculations?
- Was an error made during procedure steps with formulas and calculations where formulas were not as simple as possible or adequate space was not provided to perform calculations?

NOTE: Should these calculations or data have been verified independently to prevent this issue? If so, and if no policy existed for guidance when this type of check should be applied, consider also identifying the root cause of *no SPAC* under *Management System - Standards, Policies,* or *Administrative Controls NI.*

graphics NI:

- Was an error made while using unclear, confusing, or misleading graphs, illustrations, one-line diagrams, or system drawings in the procedure?
- Were the procedure drawings inaccurate when compared to plant reference drawings (P&IDs) or to the actual plant?

NOTE: If the plant reference drawings are wrong, consider the root cause *drawings/prints NI* under *Management System - Standards, Policies* or *Administrative Controls NI.*

no checkoff:

- Was an error made because each separate action did not have a checkoff space provided to guard against omitting significant steps? (An example is a list of valves to open or close without a separate checkoff space for each valve. A list with several valves and no checkoff spaces can lead to missing one or more valves.)

NOTE: If there is no policy on the use of checkoff spaces in procedures, also consider identifying the root cause of *no SPAC* under *Management System - Standards, Policies,* or *Administrative Controls NI.*

checkoff misused:

- Was a checkoff misused (possibly by doing several steps at once rather than doing one step, checking it off as complete, then doing the next step)?

NOTE: If a checkoff was misused, also consider identifying a root cause under the category *Management System - SPAC Not Used.*

NOTE: If no policy exists on the proper use of checkoffs, also consider identifying the root cause of *no SPAC* under the category of *Management System - Standards, Policies,* or *Administrative Controls NI.*

misused second check:

NOTE: A second check is an independent verification that a task was completed correctly.

- Was a second check required but not performed or performed in a non-independent manner?

NOTE: Also consider identifying a root cause under *Management System - SPAC Not Used* if a policy on second checking was violated.

ambiguous instructions:

- Were the instructions written so that they could be interpreted in more than one way?

- Did imprecise use of language lead to a misinterpretation of the work to be performed?

equipment identification NI:

- Did component/equipment identification or labeling in the field not agree with the identification in the procedure? (For example, the procedure might say to leave a switch in the Equipment Room "ER" position, but in the field the two switch positions are labeled "normal" and "alternate.")

NOTE: If a facility or company does not have a policy on the use of standard terminology or the use of this terminology in labeling and procedures, also consider identifying the root cause of no SPAC under *Management System - Standards, Policies,* or *Administrative Controls NI.*

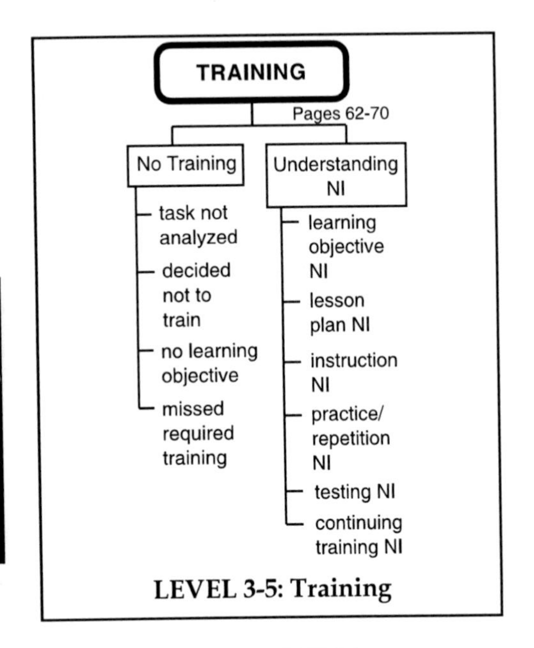

Training

TRAINING

TRAINING:

This category applies no matter what method was used to provide the training (for example: lecture, self-study, on-the-job training, or computer-based training).

- Should the person have had better training to understand the task, develop the skill needed, or maintain the knowledge and skills needed to successfully complete the task?

<u>NOTE</u>: Some causes initially considered as Training should instead be considered

as *Work Direction - Selection of Worker* if a person who was not qualified by the facility's rules was assigned to perform the work (thereby bypassing the facility's training program).

NOTE: Some causes initially considered as *Training* should instead be considered as *Procedures* if using an appropriate procedure could alleviate or reduce the need for additional training.

NOTE: Some causes initially considered as *Training* should instead be considered as *Human Engineering* if better design could have prevented the issue.

NOTE: Some causes initially considered as *Training* should instead be considered as *Work Direction - Preparation - pre-job briefing NI* if the pre-job brief should have made additional training unnecessary.

NOTE: Some causes initially considered as *Training* should instead be considered as *Management System - SPAC Not Used - comm. of SPAC NI* if a standard, policy, procedure, or administrative control was not used because management did not adequately communicate the SPAC.

No Training

No Training:

- Was there no training provided for a task that training should have been provided for?

Training (No Training)

- Was there no training for the person performing the task on a particular system or subject?
- Did the person performing the task miss required training?
- Was a subject that should have been covered in training not covered because of poor (or no) task analysis during training development?

NOTE: If the issue was related to failure of personnel to use a policy because the person wasn't trained, then consider the root cause of *comm. of SPAC NI under Management System - SPAC Not Used* instead of the *Training* category.

NOTE: If the issue was related to management not communicating their vision for the company, their concern about quality, safety, environment, or their beliefs about how the facility should be operated, then consider the root cause of *employee communications NI* under the category *Management System - Oversight/ Employee Relations* instead of the *Training* category.

task not analyzed:

- Was training not offered on the subject because no one analyzed the tasks and therefore didn't recognize the need for training on a particular task, knowledge requirement, or skill?

- Was no training offered because an incomplete task analysis failed to recognize the need for training?

NOTE: Task analysis is the process of listing all tasks or jobs that personnel perform and the requirements or knowledge and skills necessary to successfully perform those tasks.

decided not to train:

- Was training not offered because a conscious decision was made not to provide training on that task (for whatever reason).

For example, 1) a task was performed so infrequently that training was thought to be a waste of effort or 2) evaluators considered the task so simple that no training was needed.

NOTE: Consider whether pre-job briefings or walk-thrus should have been performed since a conscious decision not to provide training was made. If they should have been, consider the root causes of *pre-job briefing NI* and/or *walk-thru NI* under the category of *Work Direction - Preparation* instead of the *Training* category.

no learning objective:

- Was no training provided to the person because there were no written learning objectives for the knowledge or skills required to perform the task and, therefore, the person never learned the things needed for successful performance?

missed required training:

- Did the person performing the work miss required training and therefore did not have the knowledge or skills required?

NOTE: If the person missed required training and there was no follow-up to ensure the training was made up, consider also identifying causes under *Management System* if the training policy was not followed or if the training policy needs improvement.

Understanding
NI

Understanding NI:

If training was provided:

- Was the issue related to not understanding a task, a system, a system's response, or other needed information because the training was somehow inadequate?
- Was a person allowed to pass the training and become qualified without the knowledge or skills required to successfully perform the tasks?
- Was continuing training not provided on a frequent enough basis so that proficiency was maintained?

NOTE: If no training was provided, consider the *No Training* near-root cause category.

learning objective NI:

- Did the written learning objectives in the lesson plans fail to provide adequate training on an important task?
- Did the learning objectives fail to list the actions that the task required?
- Did learning objectives fail to explain the factors that influence performance of the task and the events that determine when the task is performed?
- Did learning objectives fail to include criteria for successful task performance?

lesson plan NI:

- Was a lesson plan deficient because it was not plant specific?
- Was a lesson plan deficient because it was technically inaccurate?
- Did the lesson plan fail to include the learning objectives, instructional media, references or aids, units of instruction, trainee evaluation methods and materials?
- Did the lesson plan specify inappropriate instructional media?

instruction NI:

- Was the presentation of the training inadequate?

- Were the lesson plans disregarded?
- Did the instructor's performance need improvement?
- Was the course material (slides, handouts, books) unavailable, not readable, or wrong?
- Was the pace of the training too fast or too slow?
- Were the prerequisite materials not covered?
- Did instructional material fail to provide the actions to be performed, the conditions under which the action is to be performed (for example, using procedures), and the standard of acceptable performance (for example, tolerances or applicable limits)?

NOTE: This root cause does NOT include inadequate pre-job instructions. Inadequate pre-job instructions should be analyzed under *Work Direction - Preparation - pre-job briefing NI.*

practice/repetition NI:

- Was training not repeated enough so that information could be learned and skills sharpened?
- Was more simulator time needed for proficiency?
- Was more practice of a skill under direct supervision needed to develop proficiency?
- Was more repetition needed to make

sure that the training became embedded in the trainee's long term memory?

testing NI:

- Did the person involved have a skill or knowledge deficiency that should have been caught by testing and corrected before allowing the person to perform work as a fully qualified team member?
- Did the testing fail to ensure mastery of required skills, knowledge, and abilities to successfully perform the work?

NOTE: If there was no policy or an insufficient policy about the testing and qualification of workers, also consider the causes under *Management System.*

continuing training NI:

- Was continuing training or retraining of personnel too infrequent, insufficient in depth, or otherwise inadequate?
- Did the person successfully complete the initial training and testing but could not perform adequately at some later date because s/he had forgotten the training or lost the skills required over time?
- If the issue involved changes in equipment, procedures, or job duties, were these changes not incorporated into the training program as quickly as they should have been?

- Was training about new or modified equipment, procedures, or other new work related information not provided to the current work force?
- If a similar problem happened before, was there a failure to incorporate lessons learned from that experience into the continuing training program?

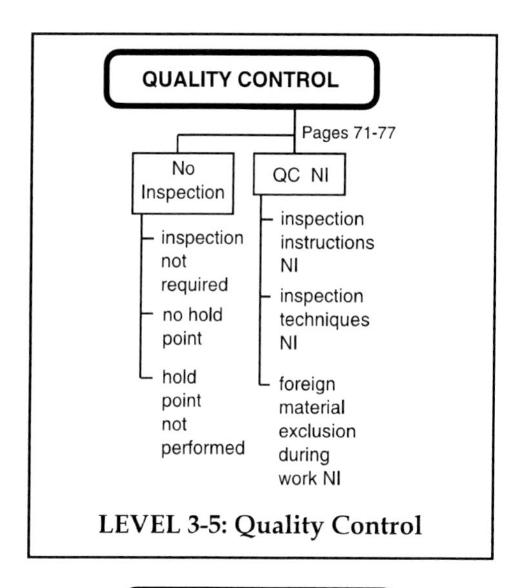

LEVEL 3-5: Quality Control

QUALITY CONTROL

QUALITY CONTROL:

This Basic Cause Category focuses on independent inspections and sampling to verify the correctness of a particularly critical step before proceeding to the next step. This Basic Cause Category does not include Self-Checking, Six Sigma or Total Quality Management initiatives (or other broad quality improvement programs). These programs are part of the *Management System* portion of the Root Cause Tree®. The focus here is on formal, independent inspection of work.

- Were tests or inspections performed but they failed to detect the issue when a reasonable test or inspection should have caught that type of issue?
- Were equipment malfunctions or maintenance difficulties not discovered because of failure to perform reasonable, independent inspections, functional tests, or quality verification checks during or after completion of work?
- Was this work so critical that someone should have been "looking over his or her shoulder" when s/he did it to make sure that no mistake was made?
- Was this work so prone to mistakes yet critical to success that it should have been inspected every time it was performed?
- Was control of the work inadequate to prevent foreign material and debris from entering undesirable locations that are inaccessible/uninspectable?

NOTE: Not all problems can be detected by inspections. You must judge the level of inspection and the amount of independence the inspector needs for the work and then decide if the inspection provided was adequate.

No Inspection

No Inspection:

- Were QC checks, functional tests, or quality verification checks not required

during or after completion of work?
- Were QC checks, functional tests, or quality verification checks required but not performed during or after completion of work?
- Was this work so critical that someone should have been "looking over their shoulder" when they did it to make sure that no mistakes were made but there was no requirement for this type of observation for this work?
- Was this work so prone to mistakes yet critical to success that it should have been inspected every time it was performed but these inspections weren't required?

inspection not required:
- Was inspection of work not performed because it had not been required (but it should have been because of the safety or production significance of the work)?
- Was this work so critical that someone should have been "looking over their shoulder" when they did it to make sure that no mistakes were made but there was no requirement for this type of work observation?
- Was this work so prone to mistakes yet critical to success that it should have been inspected every time it was performed but these inspections weren't required?

NOTE: If there was no policy requiring an inspection but there should have been an inspection, also consider the root causes under the category *Management System - SPAC NI.*

no hold point:

- Was an inspection required, but the procedure or work plan did not include an inspection hold point?

NOTE: Only use this root cause if it was possible to specify a hold point in the procedure or work plan.

NOTE: If the policy about using hold points needed improvement, also consider root causes under the category *Management System - Standards, Policies, or Admin Controls (SPAC) NI.*

hold point not performed:

- Was a required, specified inspection hold point skipped, deleted, ignored, overlooked, or for some other reason not performed?

NOTE: If performing a hold point was required by a policy or a procedure, also consider the root causes under the category *Management System - SPAC Not Used.*

QC NI:

QC NI focuses of the completeness and adequacy of the formal quality control/quality inspection program for the work.

- Was a quality inspection or verification required but some deficiency in the inspection caused the problem to be missed?
- Were improper sampling, measurement, or inspection techniques used?
- Was the inspection specified beyond the capabilities of the inspection techniques or measurement devices?
- Was an equipment problem caused by specifying inspection or testing that was not adequate or comprehensive enough to detect a problem that should have been detected?
- Was inadequate care taken during the work to ensure that quality could be documented at the job's completion (for example, failure to maintain cleanliness boundaries where final inspection is difficult or impossible)?
- Was control of the work inadequate to prevent foreign material and debris from entering undesirable locations that are inaccessible/uninspectable?

NOTE: If the inspectors could have performed the inspections, but they had not been adequately trained, consider looking at the root causes under the Training category instead of this category.

inspection instructions NI:

- Were the instructions (including any written or verbal information) for the inspection or test somehow inadequate?
- Did the Quality Verification (QV) check sheet contain too little detail?
- Should a reasonable QV check look for and detect this particular error but the inspection procedure or test was not specified?
- Did inspection instructions contain too little specific information to clearly describe the test or verification that was to be performed?

<ins>*NOTE*</ins>: If you decide that the inspection instructions need improvement, DO NOT identify additional root causes under the *Procedures* or *Communications* categories as this would cause duplicate recording of the same problem.

inspection techniques NI:

- Was the inspection specified beyond the capabilities of the inspection techniques or measurement devices?
- Did the techniques fail to isolate the proper item to be inspected to ensure proper post-inspection performance?

- Could improving the inspection technique help catch this type of issue and thereby prevent future problems?

foreign material exclusion during work NI:

- Was control of the work inadequate to prevent foreign material and debris from entering undesirable locations that are inaccessible or uninspectable (for example, the reduction gears of a steam turbine or the intake manifold of an engine)?

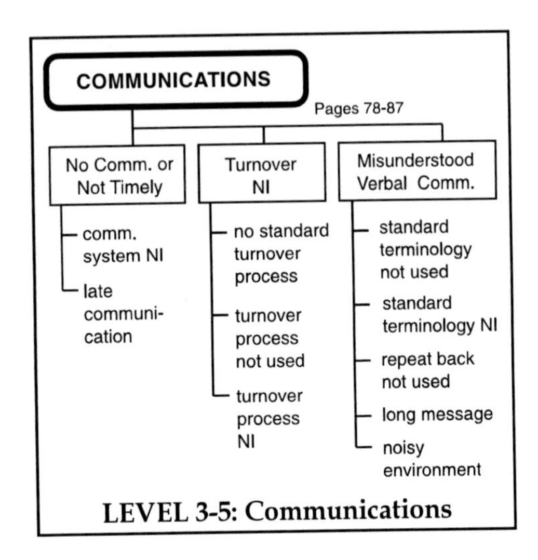

LEVEL 3-5: Communications

Communications

COMMUNICATIONS

COMMUNICATIONS:

- Did the issue include a communication error or lack of communications between people performing work?
- Was a supervisor's instruction misunderstood or misinterpreted?
- Was feedback or information from personnel performing a job misunderstood or not received by a supervisor or others involved in the job?
- Was work or shift turnover between personnel inadequate?
- If people had communicated more effectively, would the issue have been prevented?

NOTE: If a communication problem indicates poor teamwork (sometimes called crew coordination or crew resource management (CRM)), consider the *crew teamwork NI* root cause under the *Work Direction - Supervision During Work* category instead of this category.

NOTE: There is a difference between *Misunderstood Verbal Communications*, a pre-job brief with inadequate content, and poor crew teamwork. *Misunderstood Verbal Communications* is analyzed under *Communications*. Poor content in a pre-job brief is analyzed under *Work Direction - Preparation - pre-job briefing NI*. The unwillingness of subordinates to question instructions that seem wrong (lack of two-way communications) is analyzed under *Work Direction - Supervision During Work - crew teamwork NI*).

NOTE: DO NOT record problems with management's employee communication program or with employee feedback to management under the *Communications* Basic Cause Category. These types of problems should be coded under *Management System - Oversight/Employee Relations*.

NOTE: Procedures (a written form of communication) are covered under the *Procedures* Basic Cause Category and should not be analyzed here.

NOTE: The *Communications* Basic Cause Category focuses on verbal communications. Other types of communications, besides turnover, are not included at the near-root cause level. Therefore, if another type of communication error is discovered (for example, a misunderstood hand signal when directing a crane or an illegible prescription written by a doctor), it should be coded under *Communications,* and a written description of the particular facts of the issue should be included in the report or in the notes field (*) of the TapRooT® Software. Please send information about these types of communications errors to System Improvements at info@taproot.com for consideration during future revisions of the Root Cause Tree® and Dictionary. Occasionally handwritten communications also fall under the *Turnover NI* near-root cause. Also, consider root causes under the *Management System, SPAC NI* or *SPAC Not Used* if you judged that there should have been a SPAC for legibility or clarity for handwritten notes or prescriptions and there wasn't one or it wasn't used.

No Comm. or Not Timely

No Comm. or Not Timely:

- Was an issue caused by failure to communicate or by communicating too late?

comm. system NI:

This root cause is focused on communication equipment/technology.

- Was no communication made because no method or system existed for communicating?
- If a voice communication system was used, was the system inadequate for the expected communications traffic during normal and/or emergency situations that should have been anticipated? (For example, were people unable to communicate because channels were overloaded?)
- Was the tone or quality of the communication system so bad that no communication was attempted?

NOTE: If there are no procedures or training in place to support priority communications (radio discipline) using a voice communication system during an emergency, consider the causes under the *Procedures, Management System,* and *Training* Basic Cause Categories.

NOTE: If the communication failure was caused by improperly using communication hardware (for example, walkie-talkies, public address system, telephones, cell phones, sound-powered phones, etc.), then consider the causes under *Training* to determine if personnel have received appropriate training for the equipment.

late communication:

- Were communications provided too late because events happened too fast to allow time for communications?
- Was no communication provided because of time constraints that inhibited taking time to communicate?

Turnover NI

Turnover NI:

- Did incorrect, incomplete, or otherwise inadequate verbal or written turnover of information during shift/watch relief cause or fail to prevent an error?
- Did incorrect, incomplete, or otherwise inadequate turnover of information during work turnover between personnel cause or fail to prevent an error?

<ins>NOTE</ins>: If a written communication failure (not a *Procedure* issue) was a handwritten note used for turnover that was misunderstood because of legibility or clarity of the note, the issue should be recorded at the near-root cause level of *Turnover NI* and a written description of the particular facts of the issue should be included in the report or in the notes field (*) of the TapRooT® Software. Please send information about these types of written communications errors to System Improvements at info@taproot.com for consideration during future revisions of

the Root Cause Tree® and Dictionary. Also, consider root causes under the *Management System, SPAC NI* or *SPAC Not Used* if you judged that there should have been a SPAC for legibility or clarity and there wasn't one or it wasn't used.

no standard turnover process:

- Did turnover of information or work status fail because of the informal methods used?
- Would a written, formal turnover that included a certain standard and, as needed, specific information, have prevented the communication failure?
- Did the person turning over information just forget to tell the other person something that could have been remembered if it would have been written down?

turnover process not used:

- Was a standard turnover process required but not used, and, if it had been used, could it have prevented the issue?

NOTE: If the turnover process was required by a policy or procedure, look for additional root causes under the *Management System - SPAC Not Used* category.

NOTE: If there wasn't a policy requiring a standard turnover process, consider looking for additional root causes under the *Management System - Standards, Policies, or Admin Controls (SPAC) NI.*

turnover process NI:

- Could the turnover process be improved to prevent this kind of issue?

Misunderstood Verbal Comm.

Misunderstood Verbal Comm.:

- Did misunderstanding verbal communication lead to an issue?
- Did someone misunderstand something that was said?
- Did someone misinterpret what was said?

NOTE: If communication failure was not a misunderstanding but rather inadequate instructions to workers from a supervisor before a job, then the cause should be recorded as a *Work Direction - Preparation - pre-job briefing NI* root cause.

NOTE: If communication failure was not a misunderstanding but rather the failure to communicate a policy, the cause should be recorded as a *Management System - SPAC Not Used - communication of SPAC NI* root cause.

NOTE: If communication failure was not a misunderstanding but rather the direction was understood to be improper but was carried out without questioning, then the cause should be recorded as a *Work Direction - Supervision During Work - crew teamwork NI* root cause.

<u>NOTE</u>: If the communication failure was caused by improperly using communication hardware (for example, walkie-talkies, public address system, telephones, cell phones, sound-powered phones, etc.), then consider the causes under *Training* to determine if personnel have received appropriate training for the equipment.

<u>NOTE</u>: If misunderstood verbal communications occurred due to language issues, accents, or regional dialects, the issue should be coded under *Misunderstood Verbal Comm.*, and a written description of the particular facts of the issue should be included in the report or in the notes field (*) of the TapRooT® Software under the *Misunderstood Verbal Comm.* category. Please send information about these types of communications errors to System Improvements at info@taproot.com for consideration during future revisions of the Root Cause Tree® and Dictionary. Also, consider root causes under the *Management System, SPAC NI* near root cause if you judge there should be a requirement for language competency testing before hiring.

standard terminology not used:

- Could the use of standard terminology make the communication more reliable and, thereby, prevent the miscommunication that led to the issue?
- If the wrong action was taken or the wrong equipment was operated, was standard or accepted terminology not used?
- Instead of using standard terminology, was a slang term used for an item and the term was misunderstood?

NOTE: If standard terminology is not part of the facility's requirements, if the policy to use standard terminology was violated, or if standard terminology isn't stressed in training, consider looking for additional causes under the categories of *Management System - SPAC NI* or *Management System - SPAC Not Used* or *Training.*

standard terminology NI:

- Did the name for two items (drugs, processes, equipment, tools, instruments, etc.) sound alike?
- Was the name of an item easily confused with another item?
- Was there confusion because one item had two or more commonly used names?
- Was there confusion because two different items shared the same name?

repeat back not used:

- Was an issue caused by failure to repeat

back a message (to verify the message was heard and understood correctly)?

NOTE: If repeat backs are not a part of the plant's policy, if the policy was violated, or if repeat backs aren't stressed in training, look for additional causes under the categories of *Management System - SPAC NI* or *Management System - SPAC Not Used* or *Training*.

long message:

- Was a message or instruction misunderstood because it was too long and couldn't be accurately understood or remembered and, therefore, should have been broken into parts or written instead of spoken?

noisy environment:

- Was a message or instruction misunderstood because of noise interference for the listener?
- If a communication system (for example, a public address system, radios, telephones, cell phones, or sound-powered phones) was used, did background noise interfere with the listener's understanding?

NOTE: If conditions were noisy, also evaluate the impact of the noise on the thinking of those involved under the *Human Engineering - Work Environment - noisy* root cause.

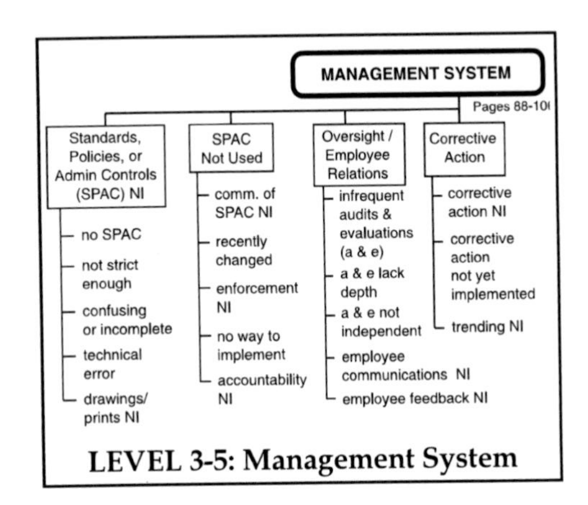

LEVEL 3-5: Management System

MANAGEMENT SYSTEM

MANAGEMENT SYSTEM:

- Could an issue have been prevented by better standards, policies, or administrative controls?
- Were policies confusing, incomplete, unclear, ambiguous, or not strict enough?
- Was a design standard or drawing inaccurate or in need of improvement?
- Was there a technical error in a standard?
- Was an issue caused by failure to use a policy or procedure?
- Did someone violate a rule?
- Was a standard not applied properly?
- Was a procedure not used when a management policy required it to be used?

- Was implementation of a policy or directive inadequate?
- Was an issue not detected and corrected by an adequate audit program when a program should have been in place?
- Were audits required that should have caught this issue, but the audits were not being performed?
- Was an issue caused by a culture of expediency that focused on getting things done rather than the quality of work or safety?
- Did employee communications fail to transmit management's concerns for quality or safety?
- Did employee concerns fail to reach the level of management that could initiate effective corrective actions?
- Was management unwilling to listen to suggestions or criticism?
- Did management fail to develop and/or implement corrective actions for known malfunctions or deficiencies?
- Would better trending of problems have led to the discovery of a generic (systemic) issue that, if corrected, could have prevented this issue?

NOTE: Investigators should be sure of the facts when recording all root causes. This is doubly true when investigating *Management System* issues. You should be able to cite specific examples, policies, or standard numbers and quote exact

Management System

wording. This type of accuracy will help convince reasonable reviewers that the causes you have identified exist and need to be promptly corrected.

Standards, Policies, or Admin Controls (SPAC) NI

Standards, Policies, or Administrative Controls (SPAC) NI:

Plant-specific standards, policies, and administrative controls (including procedures) are standardized work practices and rules. SPAC exist to minimize errors by establishing management's expectations for the ways an organization coordinates and specifies work.

- Was a new SPAC needed to prevent this issue or conform to a law?
- Was an issue caused by inadequate SPAC?
- Was an issue caused by a SPAC that did not meet the intent of a regulation or law?
- Were the SPAC confusing, incomplete, unclear, ambiguous, not strict enough, or otherwise inadequate?
- Was a design standard or drawing inaccurate or in need of improvement?
- Was there a technical error in a standard?

no SPAC:

- Was there a law that required a company SPAC but the company didn't have one?
- Was the work or situation involved significant or complicated enough to warrant some type of SPAC to ensure adequate job quality and work control but no SPAC was available?
- Do other facilities, plants, units, or similar operations have SPAC to control this type of work but there wasn't a SPAC for this facility?

not strict enough:

- Were the existing SPAC too lenient to provide adequate job quality, safety, or work control?
- Had leniency of the SPAC allowed violation of its intent?
- Did the SPAC require frequent "interpretation" that allowed lower standards to be used?
- Was the SPAC more lenient than the laws, regulations, or industry standards that should have been the basis of the SPAC?

confusing or incomplete:

- Were the SPAC confusing, hard to understand or interpret, or ambiguous?
- Were the SPAC incomplete or not specific enough?

- Did SPAC fail to address all the situations that it should have?

technical error:
- Did a technical error or incorrect facts exist in the SPAC and contribute to the issue?

drawings/prints NI:
- Was the issue caused by drawings or prints that were incorrect?
- Was the issue caused by drawings or prints that were not updated, or did they not reflect current "as built" conditions?

NOTE: Drawings are included as SPAC because they are a form of technical standard for the facility, and their continued accuracy depends largely on management's insistence on the use of the "management of change" process.

SPAC Not Used

SPAC Not Used:
- Were SPAC not used, not adhered to, not followed, or intentionally followed incorrectly?

NOTE: Reasons for not following a SPAC may not be known, but whatever the reasons, management must ensure that the SPAC are used. If audits and evaluations should have detected and reported the SPAC not being used but they did not, also consider the root causes under the *Oversight/Employee Relations* section of the *Management System* Basic Cause Category.

communication of SPAC NI:

- Were standards or policies not communicated from management down through the organization?
- Did the people involved not understand the SPAC because the SPAC was communicated inadequately?
- Did the people involved fail to understand that they were responsible for compliance with the SPAC because the SPAC was communicated inadequately?

NOTE: Inadequate communication of SPAC means that SPAC were not understood due to failure to communicate the SPAC by formal means (training, directives, or oral communication) or informal means (management support through involvement, concern, example, or vigor). If you find that the SPAC was not communicated because of inadequate management involvement, concern, example, or vigor, then also consider the root cause of *employee communications NI* under the *Management System - Oversight/ Employee Relations* category.

recently changed:

- Was this issue caused by changes in standards or directives that resulted in confusion about a SPAC?

enforcement NI:

This root cause has to do with management's actions to exercise control, influence behavior, and ensure that the person who is responsible actually follows the SPAC by holding people accountable.

- Did management sometimes reward people for the same behaviors that they would at other times punish people for?
- Was enforcement of the SPAC seen as inconsistent by the employees?
- Has enforcement of the SPAC in the past been lax?
- Has failure to follow SPAC in the past gone uncorrected or unpunished?
- Has noncompliance been accepted by supervision?
- Has it been common practice to not use or deviate from the SPAC without management's concurrence?
- Did management fail to provide positive incentives for people to follow the SPAC?
- Were positive incentives infrequently or inconsistently used?
- Did positive and negative incentives to follow the SPAC conflict?

- Was there a reward for NOT following the SPAC (for example: saving time, avoiding discomfort, peer recognition, saving effort, making the supervisor happy, or some sort of official or unofficial bonus) that should have been understood and, if possible, removed, and replaced by a greater positive reward for following SPAC put in its place?
- Did management or supervision look the other way when rules were broken?
- When supervisors or management noticed problems with worker behavior, did they fail to coach workers and thereby leave problems similar to this causal factor uncorrected?

NOTE: Management should use rewards and punishment (progressive discipline) to ensure that standards or administrative controls are used by employees in the field. However, if no standard existed, then consider the near root cause of *Standards, Policies, or Administrative Controls (SPAC) NI* rather than *enforcement NI*.

NOTE: If management attempted to enforce the SPAC but there was no way to identify who was answerable for the action required to implement the SPAC, consider the root cause category of *accountability NI* below.

NOTE: If management was not enforcing the SPAC adequately, and the internal audit and assessment program did not detect problems, also consider the root causes related to audits under the near root cause *Oversight/Employee Relations*.

no way to implement:

- Was the SPAC not followed or followed incorrectly because a method of implementation was not provided for the SPAC or because no practical way of implementing the SPAC existed?
- Was the SPAC impractical to implement because of the time and effort required to comply with it, given the level of staffing and the amount of work that was expected?
- Was there no way to implement the SPAC because of insufficient resources?

accountability NI:

This root cause has to do with people understanding who is accountable for a SPAC and management's ability to detect failures to follow SPAC by those who are accountable.

- Did a problem occur because no one was responsible, answerable, or accountable for a specific job or action that was required but not performed?
- Was there no means to clearly identify who was accountable for this particular application of the SPAC?

- Did the people involved believe that someone else was accountable or responsible for the SPAC?
- If management needs to be able to verify an action required by a SPAC, was it NOT possible for management to verify that a SPAC was followed, a check box was used, a peer check was performed correctly, or a QA check was performed?
- Does the level of accountability for the SPAC need to be increased to make people more likely to perform the desired actions because they are more answerable for their actions (for example, a signature requirement for receiving a delivery or completion of a procedure)?

NOTE: *Enforcement NI* and *accountability NI* are easy to confuse. Accountability (as defined for use with the Root Cause Tree®) has to do with the ability of management and the people involved to clearly identify who is responsible and answerable for a particular SPAC. Enforcement has to do with management's actions to exercise control and ensure that the person who is responsible actually follows the SPAC. Therefore, if you can't tell who is responsible (or answerable), or if the only way you can tell is for an accident to occur, then consider *accountability NI*. If, on the other hand, accountability is clear, but management is not taking action to ensure that the SPAC is being used, then consider *enforcement NI*. Occasionally, an investigator can find that both accountability and enforcement are root causes. In that case, both *accountability NI* and *enforcement NI* root causes should be recorded.

NOTE: If direct supervision was required to be at the job site enforcing the SPAC but they frequently were not present and, thus, accountability could not be established, in addition to *accountability NI* and *enforcement NI*, consider the root causes under *Work Direction, Supervision During Work.*

Oversight / Employee Relations

Oversight/Employee Relations:

- Did management fail to hear about the issue and their involvement was needed to ensure adequate corrective actions?
- Could the issue have been prevented by management involvement in an adequate evaluation program with timely corrective actions?
- Did failure of management's employee communications program to communicate their concerns for quality workmanship, their beliefs, safety emphasis, programmatic direction, etc., contribute to the issue?

- Did management fail to create the appropriate culture or work environment to prevent this type of issue?
- Did management fail to provide proper examples and rewards (or inconsistent examples and rewards) for quality workmanship, good safety performance, and environmental stewardship in the organization?
- Could the issue have been detected and corrected by an audit conducted by an independent, outside auditor and should this audit have been requested by management?

infrequent audits & evaluations (a & e):

- Were audits or evaluations performed too infrequently to detect system or equipment deficiencies?

NOTE: This root cause should only be used if it is judged reasonable to expect an audit or evaluation system to be in place for the affected equipment or system. Certainly, everything cannot be audited, but the effectiveness of important safety, environment, production, and quality related systems should be evaluated periodically.

NOTE: Employee observations that are part of a coordinated, documented self-evaluation or behavior based safety program can be included as audits and evaluations if the results are reported to management.

a & e lack depth:

- Was an issue not prevented by an audit or evaluation because the audits were not designed to dig to enough depth to detect system deficiencies?
- Was an issue not prevented because auditors failed to use due diligence in preparing for and performing audits and thus failed to thoroughly analyze the issue being audited?
- Was an issue not prevented by an audit or evaluation because the auditors did not dig as deeply as they should have?

NOTE: This category should only be used if an auditor performing a reasonably in-depth audit should have been able to detect the kind of difficulty that caused the issue.

a & e not independent:

- Did the internal audit program fail to detect an issue that probably would have been detected and corrected if an independent audit had been conducted?
- Was the issue caused by failure to provide an independent audit (an audit performed by someone other than the owner of the system involved)?

NOTE: This category should only be used if an independent auditor performing a reasonably in-depth audit would have detected the kind of difficulty that caused

- Did employees believe other employees had been fired, demoted, or not promoted because of expressing safety, quality, or environmental concerns?
- Did employees believe they should not report a problem until they had a solution for it?
- Were managers penalized if they didn't have answers for employee concerns when they were reported?
- Was management unwilling to listen to suggestions or criticism?

Corrective Action

Corrective Action:

- Was an issue caused by failure to provide effective corrective action for known deficiencies (recurring failures)?
- Was an issue caused by implementing inadequate corrective action?
- Was the corrective action that could have prevented the issue proposed but not implemented in a reasonable time before the issue recurred?
- Was there a failure to implement effective interim compensatory actions while waiting to implement final corrective actions?
- Would better trending of problems have led to the discovery of a generic (systemic) issue that, if corrected, could have prevented this issue?

NOTE: In this section, known deficiencies are any deficiencies that had previously been identified to supervision or management and sufficient time had passed so that effective corrective action should have been implemented. One should maintain a list of specific recurring failures to improve the consistency of root cause analysis in this category.

NOTE: If you find a *Corrective Action* near-root cause, you should also find and record the cause of the original failure that wasn't corrected and allowed the issue to happen again. These causes could be under ANY Basic Cause Category on the Root Cause Tree®.

corrective action NI:

- Was an issue caused by failure to provide effective corrective action for known deficiencies (recurring failures)?
- Was a corrective action for a known deficiency not recommended?
- Was a corrective action for a known deficiency disregarded?
- Did the corrective action address only the symptoms of a problem and fail to address the root causes?
- Did management decide to implement lower cost or otherwise different corrective actions that didn't adequately fix the previously discovered issue?

- Was an implemented interim compensatory action or corrective action unsuccessful in preventing an issue's recurrence?
- Should the failure of a corrective action have been detected by a corrective action effectiveness review (validation) but it was not checked?

corrective action not yet implemented:

- Was a corrective action that would have prevented the issue proposed, but not implemented in a reasonable time, before the issue recurred? (Reasons for failure to implement a corrective action may include delays in funding, delays in project design, abnormal length of the corrective action to implementation cycle, or lack of emphasis on the implementation of corrective actions.)
- Did failure to track the implementation of corrective actions lead to unacceptable delays in the implementation of corrective actions or failure to implement corrective actions that were recommended and approved?
- Was there a failure to implement effective interim compensatory actions while waiting to implement final corrective actions?

<u>NOTE</u>: One must allow a reasonable time for implementation of corrective actions. The time allowed should be based on the

seriousness of the issue and the scope of the work required to correct it. However, adequate interim compensatory actions should be taken while awaiting the final corrective actions. This action could include not restarting the plant or process until management judges that it is safe to do so.

trending NI:

- Would better trending of failures and root causes have led to the discovery of a generic (systemic) problem that, if corrected, should have prevented this issue?
- Was a significant trend that indicated a problem missed because the facility didn't use proper statistical process control trending techniques?

NOTE: If a trend was detected but adequate interim compensatory actions or corrective actions were not proposed, the root cause should be recorded under *corrective action NI.*

NOTE: If a trend was detected but adequate interim compensatory actions or corrective actions were proposed but were not implemented in a timely manner, the root cause should be recorded under *corrective action not yet implemented.*

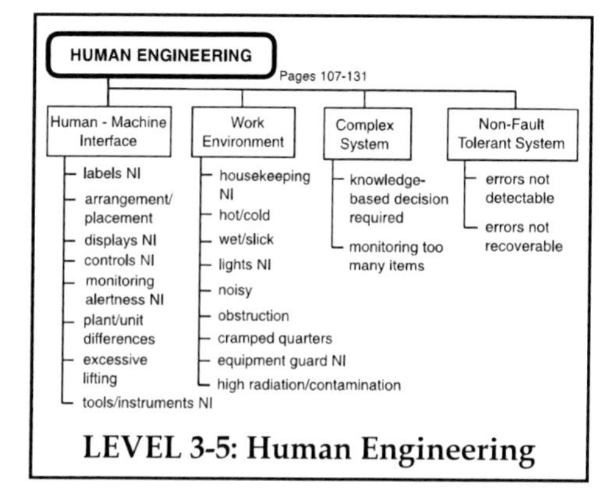

HUMAN ENGINEERING

HUMAN ENGINEERING:

- Was an issue caused by poor or undesirable human factors engineering or ergonomics?
- Did poor or undesirable human factors engineering lead a person to choose the wrong equipment, tool, valve, switch, or control when performing a task?
- Did the person need better tools, alarms, displays, or controls to successfully perform the work?
- Did the task require repetitive motion or lifting heavy objects?
- Was significant vibration present?
- Did the person have a hard time reaching or seeing an item?
- Was the person somehow confused about a component, valve, or control?

- Did the person become bored while monitoring a display or while waiting for a system response?
- Was a display misread or hard to understand?
- Did the work environment contribute to the issue?
- Was visibility an issue?
- Was there an obstruction that caused a hazard or was the workspace cramped?
- Did poor housekeeping contribute to the issue?
- Was the system hard to understand (excessively complicated)?
- Was a problem hard to detect or impossible to correct (when detecting and correcting, the type of problem should have been anticipated and allowed for by the system's designers)?
- Was the person distracted and missed a critical indication, message, or signal?
- Was a machine, equipment, process, or tool not adequately guarded to protect people from a hazard?

NOTE: For the purposes of the Root Cause Tree®, *Human Engineering* is narrowly defined as referring to causes related to four categories:

1) Human-machine interface problems [problems caused by poor human factors design of equipment interfaces, controls, tools, or jobs],

2) Poor work environment problems,
3) System complexity problems, and
4) Non-fault tolerant system problems [a system in which an error is not detectable or not recoverable].

NOTE: Finding human engineering root causes requires on-site activities. You must assess available lighting, environmental factors, space requirements, and inconsistencies with human engineering principles to be able to identify human engineering root causes. The most important question to ask is, "What does a person need to successfully complete this task?" The most difficult part of investigating *Human Engineering* difficulties is the attitude of "It has always been done this way." That is why an outside or unfamiliar set of eyes (perhaps an outside human factors expert) may be needed to analyze difficult *Human Engineering* issues.

NOTE: The best trade-off between easy-to-use designs, procedures, and training is difficult to judge, but the three are certainly interrelated. Multiple, overlapping corrective actions that include human factors, training, and procedures are better than a single, partially effective solution. Therefore, you should also consider the causes under the *Training* and *Procedures* Basic Cause Categories when you consider *Human Engineering* causes.

NOTE: All human factors design problems are included under *Human Engineering* rather than under *Design*. The *Design* category is only for equipment design issues that cause equipment failures NOT related to human performance.

Human - Machine Interface

Human-Machine Interface:

- Was an issue caused by poor coordination or interaction of personnel with the equipment, systems, facilities, or instrumentation with which they work?
- Was an issue caused by poor or undesirable human factors engineering or ergonomics?
- Did a poor or undesirable human-machine interface lead a person to choose the wrong equipment, tool, valve, switch, or control when performing a task?
- Would better labels or warning signs have prevented the issue?
- Could a more user-friendly design have prevented the issue?
- Did the person need better tools, alarms, displays, or controls to successfully perform the work?
- Was the person somehow confused about a component, valve, or control?
- Did the person miss an important signal, alarm, changing parameter, or message that needed to be noticed?

- Did the task require repetitive motion?
- Did the task require lifting heavy objects (beyond what was reasonable)?
- Was significant vibration present?
- Did the person have a hard time reaching or seeing an item?
- Was a guard needed to protect the person operating a piece of equipment or a tool from a hazard?
- Was the person somehow confused about a component, valve, or control?
- Was the person distracted and missed a critical indication, message, or signal?
- Did the person become bored while monitoring a display or while waiting for a system response?

labels NI:

- Are labels or warning signs missing?
- Would better labels or warning signs have prevented the issue?
- Are connections for leads on equipment not clearly labeled?
- Was the current equipment setting or default mode unclear because the equipment or switches were not labeled?
- Are the labels hard to read? That is:
  - Not easily read under operations and maintenance conditions.
  - Obscured by other equipment.
  - Not visible when moving a control.
  - Of a color that blends in with the equipment background.

- Poor contrast between the letters and the label background.
- Are the labels unclear or ambiguous? That is:
  - Not located close to the items they identify.
  - Do not use unique names, acronyms, abbreviations, and part/system numbers created using company or industry standard nomenclature.
  - Inconsistent with the words used in the procedures.
  - Not distinguishable between units in multi-unit plants.
  - Not distinguishable between similar but different types of portable equipment that can easily be confused.
  - Discrete functional control positions (on/off) are not identified.
  - Direction to move a control for a desired outcome (for example, increase/decrease) is not identified.
  - Unclear as to setting or default mode?
- Are warning signs difficult to read or understand?

arrangement/placement:

This root cause has to do with the physical location of equipment, displays, and controls.

- Did poor arrangement, placement, or situation of equipment, displays, or controls contribute to an issue?

- Were gauges, alarms, or displays placed so that reading them was difficult?
- Were gauges, alarms, or displays placed so high that reading them with bifocal glasses was difficult?
- Was the relationship not obvious between which display or alarm went with which control?
- Did the control/display relationship need improvement?
- If a control was accidentally actuated (bumped), was the control not:
  - Located,
  - Oriented, or
  - Guarded

  to minimize accidental actuation?
- Were valves or other controls out of reach of those required to operate them?
- Did the arrangement or placement of valve controls cause musculoskeletal problems because operating the valves or controls was awkward or caused unsafe postures?
- Were identical storage bins for similar components/parts or medicines placed side-by-side and easily confused?
- If a person was required to see something, was his view blocked?

displays NI:

- Could the information have been displayed differently to be better understood?

- Did confusing, inadequate, or unclear instrumentation, gauges, or alarms cause the issue?
- Did confusing, inadequate, or unclear CRT (cathode ray tube), DCS (distributed control system), or other types of computer based displays cause the issue?
- Were computer based menus unclear or difficult to navigate?
- Was the current equipment setting or default mode unclear because of the display?

NOTE: Also consider *labels NI* and *controls NI* and choose the most applicable category based on the type of equipment and the problem encountered.

- Was there no display to indicate that the equipment was in a safe or fail-safe mode or in an abnormal mode?
- Was essential information missing from a display?
- Was critical system information not available from displays? (For example: changes in equipment status, device failure, battery failure, dangerous conditions, safe operating limits being exceeded, error messages/codes.)
- Does the gauge's or computer display's face graduation & numbering fail to relate the readings in a practical way to the user's task? In other words, was the issue caused by:

- The display's graduations being inconsistent with the degree of precision and accuracy needed?
- Values that require conversion?
- Dimensions/units not provided or labeled inaccurately or confusingly?
- Using percentages when using numeric values would be more meaningful?
- The scale of the display spanning a range different from the range needed to measure the parameter?

- Was an alarm needed to attract attention to a change in a key system variable?
- Did the alarm fail to attract the attention of those who needed to respond?
- Were alarms overlooked because of previous, frequent nuisance alarms?
- Were alarms overlooked because there were an excessive number of alarms (many of them unimportant) that overloaded the person's ability to perceive them and respond?
- Were alarms or annunciators unclear, ambiguous, or difficult to interpret?
- Did the alarm tiles or annunciators have:
  - Long, unclear, or confusing messages?
  - Inconsistent or non-standard abbreviations or acronyms?
  - Incorrect messages or titles?
- If information was displayed on printouts:

- Did the printout fail to provide the information in a format so that the person using it could readily understand the information?
- Was the information on the printout somehow misleading or inaccurate?
- Was information on the printout difficult to find?

- Did the information provided by the display fail to support the operator's mental model of the system?

NOTE: If better training was needed to improve the operator's mental model, consider the *Training* Basic Cause Category.

controls NI:

- Did inadequate controls contribute to the issue?
- Was a control so complex that it contributed to the issue?
- Could the system reasonably have been designed with simpler controls to prevent or reduce the chance of error?
- Was a control accidentally operated because of the similarity of other controls around it?
- Did controls need mistake-proofing to prevent unintentional or incorrect actuation?
- Was a control inadequate because it:
  - Lacks sufficient range of control?
  - Is difficult to adjust with the required level of precision?

- Was difficult to recognize the control's function? (For example: confusing grouping of controls; similar controls that look alike and are not color coded and/or shape coded to distinguish difference in function or purpose; or shape does not correspond to the person's mental model.)
- Is not the type of control normally anticipated for that purpose? (For example, controls NI would include a valve that must be turned clockwise to increase flow.)
- Causes musculoskeletal problems (for example, carpal tunnel syndrome or a back injury)?

- Did the machine fail to have adequate emergency stop controls?
- Was there a lack of feedback as to the controls' position or response?
- Was the control hard to identify or operate when wearing commonly used protective clothing / personal protective equipment?
- Was the current control setting or default mode unclear because of the control shape or indicator type?

NOTE: Also consider *labels NI* and *displays NI* and choose the most applicable category based on the type of equipment and the problem encountered.

- Did a machine, equipment, or process lack adequate safety controls/devices (such as machine guards, light curtains, or two-hand operated controls) to prevent the operator from being caught in pinch points, moving parts, or other hazards while controlling/operating the equipment?

NOTE: If the guard was removed, consider the *Management System, Work Direction,* and *Training* categories rather than this root cause.

NOTE: If the guard was part of a hand held tool or instrument, consider the *tools/instruments NI* root cause rather than this root cause.

NOTE: If the moving parts/pinch point hazard was not due to the operation of the equipment but rather was a hazard to anyone in the area (the general workforce, visitors, or the general public), consider the *equipment guard NI* root cause under the *Work Environment* near root cause rather than this root cause.

NOTE: If a control was not reachable or if there was a control/display relationship problem, consider the root cause *arrangement/placement* instead of the root cause *controls NI.*

NOTE: If a control or an adjustment could not be used because there wasn't enough room to get access, consider the root cause *cramped quarters* under the *Work*

Environment near root cause instead of the *controls NI* root cause.

monitoring alertness NI:

- Could the difficulty be attributed to loss of performance over time while monitoring?
- Did the person get bored while waiting for a signal and fail to respond when the signal was present?
- If a signal was missed, did the task require constantly watching a stable indicator for more than 20 minutes?

NOTE: Human performance studies indicate that alertness during monitoring diminishes over time. The rate that alertness declines depends on the type of monitoring and the rate at which signals are received. In general, the odds of missing a signal increase rapidly after 20 to 30 minutes of monitoring a relatively unchanging indicator. This is called the "vigilance decrement." Therefore, keep continuous monitoring with little or no control action to a very short duration or use other backup (or primary) means of monitoring.

plant/unit differences:

This root cause has nothing to do with units of measure. Instead, it has to do with people becoming confused or making mistakes when people use similar but not identical equipment or devices.

- Did differences in equipment, displays, or controls between the different plants/ production units contribute to the issue?
- Did an individual think that the equipment, displays, or controls were the same as another facility, unit, process, or area that they were familiar with and, therefore, make a mistake because this facility was different (non-standard)? [Errors are more common when personnel change assignments from one unit/plant to another (or work on a temporary basis in a different unit/plant) where there are slight but significant differences between the production units/plants/equipment.]
- Was a device or equipment similar to another model but its operations, controls, or displays were different and this caused the issue?
- Was a device or equipment similar to another model but its default mode or fail-safe mode was different and this caused an issue?
- Did a new device or piece of equipment look like an older model but its operations, controls, or displays were different and this caused an issue?

excessive lifting:

- Was the issue related to excessive lifting or force to move an object?

- Did the task require repetitive motion (lifting, twisting, bending, etc.) that lead to a musculoskeletal problem?
- Was significant vibration present that caused a musculoskeletal problem?

NOTE: A good reference to decide if the lifting was excessive is the NIOSH Lifting Guidelines (Applications Manual for the Revised NIOSH Lifting Equation (PB94-176930), US Department of Health & Human Services). Download it from the NIOSH web site: www.cdc.gov/niosh/pdfs/94-110.pdf.

tools/instruments NI:

This category focuses on hand-tools and surgical instruments, not instrumentation (sensors, electronic instrumentation, or display panels).

- Was the tool so difficult to use that the person made an error?
- Was the tool shaped wrong so that it was uncomfortable to use or caused musculoskeletal problems?
- Did the tool require excessive force to operate?
- Did the tool transmit excessive vibration to the user?
- Did the shape or construction of the instrument/tool cause the user to make mistakes or to perform inaccurately?
- Was the correct tool so difficult to use that the person chose an inappropriate

tool that didn't work well but seemed easier to use?
- Did the tool have unguarded pinch points or other hazardous surfaces that should have been guarded?

<u>NOTE</u>: If guards had been removed, consider the *Management System, Work Direction,* and *Training* categories.

<u>NOTE</u>: If the tool was the wrong tool to use for this work and the proper tool was available and would have prevented this problem, then consider the root causes under the Basic Cause Categories of *Procedures, Training,* and *Work Direction* instead of this root cause.

Work Environment

Work Environment:
- Was the work environment not conducive to good human performance?
- Did poor housekeeping, poor footing, obstructions or slippery surfaces, contribute to the issue?
- Did restricted visibility or inadequate lighting contribute to the issue?
- Did extreme heat or cold contribute to the issue?
- Did high radiation or contamination, hazardous or toxic emissions contribute to the issue?
- Did excessive noise contribute to the issue?

- Were hazardous equipment, machinery, or processes not adequately guarded to prevent injury to the general workforce?

NOTE: Human performance can be degraded by environmental stressors. The investigator should walk through the work areas and interview personnel involved to determine whether any of these stressors were present at the time the error was made.

NOTE: If poor visibility (that was caused by conditions other than lighting) contributed to the issue, use the note field at the near-root cause category of *Work Environment* to record the details of the cause and send the information about the issue to System Improvements at info@taproot.com for consideration for future changes to the Root Cause Tree®.

housekeeping NI:

- Did poor housekeeping contribute to the issue (for example, tripping over trash or tools that should have been stored)?

hot/cold:

Was an issue caused by excessive exposure of personnel to hot or cold environments (for example, heat exhaustion or numbness from cold)?

- Did hurrying to get out of an excessively hot or cold environment contribute to the issue?

<u>NOTE</u>: If a person was scheduled for excessive amounts of time in a hot or cold environment, also consider the root cause under *Work Direction - Preparation - scheduling NI.*

<u>NOTE</u>: If a person did not have proper clothing for hot/cold conditions that should have been anticipated by the supervisor, consider the root causes under *Work Direction - Preparation.*

wet/slick:

- Was an issue caused by a slippery surface that should have been:
  - Mopped up and dried?
  - Cleaned/treated to make it less slippery?
  - Roped off or otherwise isolated to keep people off until the condition could be corrected?
- Was the issue caused by adverse conditions that were the result of rain or snow (for example, slipping on ice that should have been removed)?

<u>NOTE</u>: If a person did not have proper footwear for wet/slick conditions that should have been anticipated by the supervisor, consider the root causes under *Work Direction - Preparation.*

lights NI:

- Did bad lighting (too much, too little, or glare producing) contribute to the issue?

NOTE: If poor visibility was caused by conditions other than lighting, use the note field at the near-root cause category of *Work Environment* to record the details of the cause.Send information about the issue to System Improvements at info@taproot.com for consideration to improve the Root Cause Tree® Dictionary.

noisy:

- Was an issue caused by diminished human performance due to excessive noise (for example, inability to hear an alarm due to high ambient noise levels)?
- Did the person involved have trouble concentrating because of the noise level?
- Was hearing protection required in a control room or a facility where detailed troubleshooting and emergency diagnosis was performed?
- Was the person distracted by the noise of the process?

NOTE: This root cause does not include communication difficulties caused by noise. For communication problems caused by noise, see the *Communications*

- *Misunderstood Verbal Communications - noisy environment* root cause.

obstruction:

- Did the person hit his or her head or another part of his or her body on an obstruction that protruded into the normally expected walkway or workspace (for example, a pipe that crosses a walkway at about head level)?
- Did an obstruction (other than by bad housekeeping) create a tripping hazard (for example, a pipe that crosses a walkway at about ankle level)?

cramped quarters:

- Did working in cramped quarters contribute to the issue?
- Was the workspace too small for the people to perform the work?
- Could an adjustment not be made or could a control not be used because there wasn't enough room to get access?
- Did cramped quarters lead to excessive stress on the musculoskeletal system?

equipment guard NI:

- Was equipment, machinery, or a hazardous process not guarded?
- Did guards need improvement to prevent injury to the general workforce, visitors, or the general public?

- If equipment is portable, is the equipment insufficiently protected so that it could be damaged when being moved?

NOTE: If the guard was removed, consider the *Management System, Work Direction,* and *Training* categories rather than this root cause.

NOTE: If the issue was related to someone operating a piece of equipment, machinery, or tool rather than someone just being near the equipment, consider the root causes of *controls NI* or *tools/instruments NI* under the *Human-Machine Interface* near root cause rather than this root cause.

high radiation/contamination:

- Did high radiation or radioactive, toxic, or hazardous chemical contamination contribute to an issue by causing personnel to hurry to reduce exposure?
- Did high radiation or radioactive, toxic, or hazardous chemical contamination contribute to an issue by requiring protective clothing that diminished performance?

Complex System

Complex System:

- Was an issue caused by the system being excessively complex or complicated?

- Was a person confused by a complicated set of controls and displays?
- Was a mistake made because someone was confused by the system complexity?
- Was a knowledge-based decision (see explanation in next definition) required to respond to a situation that should have been covered by the procedure or made common practice by repetitive training?
- Were too many variables acting at once causing confusion or indecisiveness?
- Were personnel required to monitor too many items or variables at once, causing personnel to miss or overlook needed information?

NOTE: If adequate training would have reduced the chance of error by teaching personnel how to use the complex system, then also consider the root causes under *Training* in addition to or instead of this near root cause.

NOTE: If a good procedure would have provided the guidance to successfully perform the work in spite of a complex system, then consider the root causes under *Procedures* in addition to or instead of this near root cause.

knowledge-based decision required: Knowledge-based decisions require understanding and knowledge of a system, the interaction of different parts of the system, and variables affecting the system. These decisions are not reflex in nature and are not simply based on trained or developed reaction to rules and, therefore, have a potential to result in more errors. For more information on decision making models and knowledge-based decisions, refer to Jens Rassmussen's paper "On the Structure of Knowledge - a Morphology of Mental Models in a Man-Machine System Context" (RISO-M-2192) (Riso National Laboratory, DK-4000, Rockilde, Denmark) and his book, *Information Processing and Human-Machine Interface, An Approach to Cognitive Engineering* (North-Holland, New York).

- Did a complex system require a decision by a person with little or no support from procedures or insufficient training to be able to instinctively react as required for a successful outcome?
- Could better design be reasonably expected to eliminate the need for this higher level knowledge and decision making?
- Could a good procedure provide the guidance necessary to successfully perform the work, yet none was available?

NOTE: If adequate training would have reduced the chance of error by teaching personnel how to use the complex system, then also consider the root causes under *Training* in addition to or instead of this root cause.

NOTE: If a good procedure would have provided the guidance to successfully perform the work in spite of a complex system, then consider the root causes under *Procedures* in addition to or instead of this root cause.

monitoring too many items:

- Were personnel required to monitor too many items or variables at one time, causing personnel to overlook or fail to notice needed information?
- Did a person ignore displays or indications because they were concentrating on a single display when they were required to monitor many displays or indications?

NOTE: Experience indicates personnel are much more apt to make mistakes by overlooking items if they are required to actively monitor multiple variables (pressure, temperature, flow, distance, time, etc.) at once. How many are too many? That depends on the work, the stress, the skill of the person, and the senses involved. As a rule of thumb, if a person has to "simultaneously" monitor 3 or more items, it is probably too many. The person investigating this root cause may want to consult with a human factors expert to evaluate the difficulty of the monitoring task and decide if excessive numbers of variables were being monitored.

Non-Fault Tolerant System

Non-Fault Tolerant System:

- Were errors undetectable?
- Did a system design prevent discovered errors from being corrected before a failure or incident occurred?

errors not detectable:

- Were errors not detectable (by way of alarm, meter reading, visible indication, audible warning, etc.) during or after their occurrence?

NOTE: It is unreasonable to expect all systems or equipment to have alarms or detectable errors, but important safety related equipment should make errors detectable.

errors not recoverable:

- Were errors not recoverable if discovered before an incident occurred?

NOTE: Important safety related equipment should be designed so that detected errors can be recovered before a major system failure occurs.

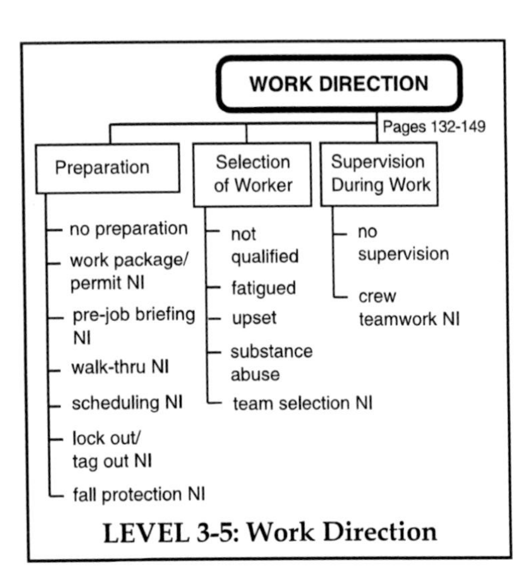

LEVEL 3-5: Work Direction

Work Direction

WORK DIRECTION

WORK DIRECTION:

Before answering the questions for the *Work Direction* section, identify the supervisor, team leader, or person-in-charge for the work. Then you can answer the following questions:

- Was an issue caused by failure to perform adequate preparation (including job plans or walk-thrus) for a job?
- Was the work plan, work permit, hazard assessment, risk assessment, or other job planning tool or paperwork inadequate?
- Was a better pre-job brief needed?

- Was too much work scheduled for the time available and/or staffing levels?
- Was the issue related to any work schedule conflicts or inadequate scheduling of work?
- Was a lock out/tag out inadequate?
- Was fall protection inadequate for the work?
- Was an issue caused by worker(s) being incapable of performing their assigned task?
- Was someone assigned to a job who was too impaired to perform the task accurately? (They may be impaired by fatigue, emotional issues, prescription or over-the-counter medications, or illegal drugs, etc.)
- Was an issue caused by poor teamwork [sometimes called crew coordination or crew resource management (CRM)]?
- Did team members fail to question improper readings or indications because of the supervisor's or another team member's forcefulness?
- Were directions by the supervisor understood to be improper but were carried out without questioning?
- Did the supervisor see a problem in the way work was being performed but did not correct it?
- Should the supervisor or team leader have prevented the issue by supervising the work while it was in progress?

- Could improved planning or supervision have prevented the issue?

NOTE: Almost every accident could be prevented if a supervisor had 20/20 foresight. However, one should only expect reasonable amounts of preparation and supervision when analyzing issues under the work direction category.

Preparation

Work Direction (Preparation)

Preparation:

- Was an issue caused by failure to perform adequate preparation/planning (including job plans or walk-thrus) for a job?
- Was the work plan, work permit, hazard assessment, risk assessment, or other job planning tool or paperwork inadequate?
- Was the pre-job brief by the supervisor or person-in-charge inadequate?
- Was too much work scheduled for the time available and/or staffing levels?
- Was the work incompatible with a rule, regulation, technical specification, safety requirement, or other requirement or condition to ensure successful performance?
- Was scheduling of periodic testing or surveillance too infrequent or at times not compatible with plant operating status?
- Did outage, turn-around, or maintenance

schedules require work that was incompatible with other work or plant conditions?

- Did the work management and tracking system fail to provide enough warning (look-ahead time) to allow preparation of permits and work packages?
- Was scheduling of the task involved contrary to that contained in a work management and tracking system?
- Was scheduling somehow inadequate to ensure success?
- Was a lock out/tag out inadequate?
- Was fall protection inadequate for the work?

NOTE: If the supervisor or person-in-charge had not been trained on the tasks to be performed and the methods to prepare employees to perform work, also consider the root causes under the *Training* Basic Cause Category.

Work Direction (Preparation)

no preparation:

- Did the supervisor or person-in-charge not provide any preparation (instructions, job plan, walk-thru, etc.) for work to be performed?

NOTE: If there was preparation, even if it needed improvement, do not use the *no preparation* root cause. Instead use the appropriate root cause below, or make a note about the problem at the *Preparation* near-root cause level if the problem is not covered by the categories below.

work package/permit NI:

- Was an issue caused by failure to develop adequate job plans, permits, or work packages?
- Was the work plan, work permit, hazard assessment, risk assessment, or other job planning tool or paperwork inadequate?
- Did the work package, work permit, or other paperwork to authorize and specify the work list the wrong equipment, wrong work site, or wrong methods to perform the work? (For example, a surgery package that lists the wrong body part for the surgery.)
- Was the sequence wrong in the work package?
- Was required coordination between work groups not mentioned in the work package?
- Were safety precautions and warnings left out of the work package?
- Did the supervisor or person-in-charge provide the wrong work package?
- Was the wrong procedure referenced by the work package?
- Did the work package violate any standards, procedures, or policies?
- Did the work package fail to require a lock out/tag out or any other safety equipment, personal protective

equipment, safeguards, or risk controls when they should have been required?

- Did the work order/job requirements fail to include acceptance criteria for the work?
- Were acceptance criteria in the work package inadequate?
- Did the permit or work package fail to comply with laws, regulations, industry standards, or company policies?
- Were there any other problems that caused the work package or permit to be incomplete, inaccurate, unsafe, unusable, or unsuccessful?

pre-job briefing NI:

- Did the supervisor or person-in-charge not hold a pre-job brief when one should have been held?
- Was important information that should have been covered omitted from the pre-job brief?
- Was the pre-job brief incorrect, incomplete, or otherwise inadequate such that the workers did not have all the information needed to perform the job correctly?
- Did the pre-job brief fail to highlight critical steps (a critical step is a step with no way to correct an error if one is made)?
- Did people not attend the pre-job brief that should have been in attendance?

NOTE: Not every job will have a pre-job brief. Also, supervisors cannot be expected to have 20-20 foresight. You must assess the adequacy of the pre-job brief given the amount of risk that was apparent.

walk-thru NI:

- Did the supervisor or person-in-charge not walk the workers through the steps required to perform an infrequently occurring, complex, or high-risk task?
- If a walk-thru was performed, did the supervisor not show the location of equipment, how to operate equipment, proper sequence of steps, etc. for the specific task?
- Did the supervisor not show the worker the actual equipment that was to be used for the job?

NOTE: Walk-thrus should be required for the most complex jobs, especially if they are performed infrequently. Walk-thrus may be performed at the job site or in a simulator that's identical to the actual work site.

scheduling NI:

- Did an employee make a mistake while rushing (because of excessive workload) to perform a task that probably would have been performed correctly if the employee wasn't rushed?

- Was it clear that too few workers were assigned to successfully accomplish the work?
- Did the schedule result in excessive overtime?
- Was the shift schedule in need of improvement to reduce worker fatigue?
- Do the hours assigned to a worker violate laws or industry standards?
- Was more than 16 hours worked in a row?
- Was the person called in 8 or more hours early to start work?
- Was the work incompatible with a rule, regulation, technical specification, safety requirement, or other condition to ensure successful performance?
- Was scheduling of periodic testing or surveillance too infrequent or at times not compatible with plant operating status?
- Did outage, turn-around, or maintenance schedules require work that was incompatible with other work or plant conditions?
- Was scheduling of the task involved contrary to that contained in a work management and tracking system?
- Was scheduling somehow inadequate to ensure success?

lock out/tag out NI:

- Was a lock out required but not performed?
- Did the supervisor or person-in-charge not ensure the adequacy of a lock out?
- Was an issue the result of an incorrect tag out or failure to lock out all necessary equipment or parts of equipment before the work?
- Was a lock (or locks) removed while work was still in progress?
- Was a lock out inadequate?
- Did the lock out not secure all sources of energy that could cause harm?

NOTE: Consider *Management System-SPAC NI* if the policy requiring lock out/tag out was inadequate or did not meet regulatory requirements.

NOTE: Consider *Management System-SPAC Not Used* if the policy for lock out/tag out was violated.

fall protection NI:

- Was fall protection required but not used?
- Did the supervisor or person-in-charge not ensure the adequacy of the fall protection in use?
- Was an issue the result of an incorrect application of fall protection equipment?
- Did the workers not know about the requirement for fall protection?

- Was fall protection equipment unavailable or inadequate?
- Was fall protection needed but, for whatever reason, not used?
- Was fall protection not used or used improperly because of inadequate points to secure the protection?
- Did workers use inappropriate fall protection devices?
- Did fall protection fail due to inadequate equipment, harnesses, or tie-off points?

NOTE: Also consider *Management System-SPAC NI* if the policy requiring fall protection equipment was inadequate or did not meet regulatory requirements.

NOTE: Also consider *Management System-SPAC Not Used* if the policy requiring fall protection was violated.

NOTE: Also consider the root causes under *Training* if the workers didn't know about the requirements for fall protection or they didn't understand how to use the fall protection equipment.

Selection of Worker

Selection of Worker:

- Did the supervisor or person-in-charge not select capable workers to perform the job?
- Did the employee make an error

while performing the task because the employee was not fully qualified to perform the task?

- Was an issue caused by worker(s) being incapable of performing their assigned task?
- Was someone assigned to a job that was too impaired to perform the task accurately? (They may be impaired by fatigue, emotional issues, prescription or over-the-counter medications, or illegal drugs, etc.)
- Did personality conflicts lead to problems performing the work?
- Was someone assigned to work who the supervisor should have seen was not fit-for-duty?
- Did the supervisor assign unqualified workers because qualified workers were not available?

You must judge that it was reasonable for the supervisor to detect the problem with the worker. Some examples of incapable workers are: workers who are not trained or certified for a particular job; workers who are not alert due to working excessive overtime; workers who are obviously emotionally upset; workers who have impaired capabilities due to substance abuse problems; or workers incapable of working together.

not qualified:

This root cause has to do with the assignment by the supervisor of fully qualified workers to a task. A "qualified" worker is one who has passed all training and testing to be certified/licensed/found competent to perform the work. The requirements for qualification may be from the company's policy, the union's apprenticeship program, a certifying/licensing/competency testing agency's requirements, an educational institution's testing, or the laws and regulations of a particular government body.

- Did the employee make an error while performing the task because the employee was not fully qualified to perform the task?
- Did the worker NOT have the required license, competency certification, or credentials to perform the work?
- Did the supervisor assign unqualified workers because qualified workers were not available at the time?

NOTE: If scheduling did not provide enough qualified workers for the work scheduled on a particular shift, consider *Work Direction-scheduling NI.*

NOTE: If the supervisor violated company policies by assigning unqualified workers, consider the root causes under *Management System-SPAC Not Used.*

fatigued:

- Did working excessive overtime, working a second job, or other factors that would cause the employee to be fatigued cause the employee to fail to be alert and therefore have difficulties when performing the task?
- Was the overtime above regulatory requirements or industry limits and this led to problems performing the work?
- Had the person worked an excessive number of hours and this caused problems with the work?
- Did the person report to the supervisor that s/he was too fatigued to work but the person was not relieved or replaced?
- Did the person report to the supervisor that s/he had a sleep disorder and that s/he felt too fatigued to work but s/he was not relieved or replaced?
- Did the supervisor see the person exhibit periods of "microsleep" prior to the problem but didn't take action? (Microsleep is brief intrusions of sleep typically repeated at 5-15 second intervals with slow eye rolling movements, repeated eye closures, head bobbing, and mental incapacitation.
- Did the supervisor see the person exhibit "Automatic Behavior Syndrome" but didn't take action? (Automatic Behavior Syndrome occurs when a person sleeps

with eyes wide open in a blank, fixed, zombie like gaze, and the person is mentally incapacitated.)

- Was the worker so fatigued that the supervisor should have observed the worker's excessive fatigue and taken action such as assigning someone else to perform the work?

NOTE: If excessive fatigue was a result of scheduled overtime or bad shift schedules, also consider the root cause of *Work Direction - Preparation - scheduling NI.*

NOTE: If the supervisor violated a company policy by assigning excessive overtime or not providing a relief for a worker who was too fatigued to perform the job, consider the root causes under *Management System-SPAC Not Used.*

upset:

- Did the employee have difficulties when performing the task because of being emotionally upset and the supervisor or person-in-charge should have detected this before assigning the work?
- Was the supervisor or person-in-charge aware of personal life problems that could cause performance difficulties, yet still assigned the worker to complex or safety related work or other work that required high precision or high reliability?

Work Direction (Selection of Worker)

substance abuse:

- Did the employee have difficulties when performing the task because the employee had impaired capabilities due to substance abuse problems and the supervisor or person-in-charge was aware or should have been aware of the problem?
- Was the person taking legal medications that degraded performance and the condition should have been apparent to the supervisor or reported to the supervisor by the employee?

team selection NI:

- Did the supervisor or person-in-charge assign the wrong mixture of expertise or experience of qualified workers?
- Did the supervisor or person-in-charge assign people with known preexisting personal conflicts between them that kept them from working together effectively?
- Did the supervisor or person-in-charge assign a worker or workers without the physical capability to perform the task?
- Did the supervisor or person-in-charge assign a worker or workers with known pre-existing condition(s) (for example, fear of heights or claustrophobia) or a previous work limiting injury (or injuries) (for example, a previous back

injury or rotator cuff surgery) that should not have been assigned to this work?

Supervision During Work

Supervision During Work:

- Was a reasonable level of supervision NOT provided?
- Did the supervisor, team leader, or person-in-charge not provide adequate support, coverage, oversight, or supervision during the job?
- Was poor response by the operating team caused by poor teamwork [sometimes called crew coordination or crew resource management (CRM)]?
- Did team members not question improper readings or indications because of the leader's or another team member's forcefulness?
- Were directions by the person-in-charge understood to be improper but were carried out without questioning?
- Did the person-in-charge see a problem in the way work was being performed but left the problem uncorrected?

<u>NOTE</u>: One must judge what level of supervision was necessary by evaluating the safety and production importance of the job and the risk that the job represents to people, company finances, the environment, and customer satisfaction.

NOTE: Guidelines for reasonable level of supervision should be provided to supervisors and should be part of first-line supervisor or team leader training. This training should include guidelines on how much time to spend directly supervising work at the job site and the role of the supervisor when observing work. If the guidance is not provided or is inadequate, consider the root causes under *Management System* if the guidance needs improvement or is not used. Consider the root causes under *Training* if first line supervisory training about this guidance is not provided or needs improvement.

no supervision:

- Was there no supervision, and would this issue have been prevented by a reasonable level of supervision at the worksite?
- Should the person-in-charge have followed the job or provided support, coverage, or oversight but didn't?

NOTE: If there was supervision, even if it needed improvement, do not use the *no supervision* root cause. Instead use the root cause below (if appropriate), or make a note about the problem at the *Supervision During Work* near-root cause level if the problem is not covered by the root cause below.

crew teamwork NI:

- Was poor response by the operating team caused by poor teamwork?
- Did team members not question improper readings or indications because of the person-in-charge's or another team member's forcefulness?
- Were directions by the person-in-charge understood to be improper but were carried out without questioning?
- Did the whole operating team focus on one problem and not attend to the other plant requirements?
- Did the person-in-charge become so focused on a single problem that the person-in-charge lost sight of the overall plant status (big picture)?
- Did the person-in-charge see a problem in the way work was being performed but left the problem uncorrected?
- Did peers notice a problem but fail to mention it to the person involved or the supervisor?
- Did the supervisor fail to coach workers when a problem was noticed and left a problem uncorrected?

NOTE: If the supervisor or person-in-charge saw people violating standards, procedures, or policies and did not correct them, also consider the root cause *Management System - SPAC Not Used - enforcement NI.*

Glossary

>	Greater Than
A & E	Audits and Evaluations
Admin	Administrative
Comm	Communication
CRT	Cathode Ray Tube
DCS	Distributed Control System
Equip	Equipment
ER	Equipment Room or Emergency Room
Hold Point	A step in a procedure that requires an inspection before the worker can move on to the next step. Therefore, at that point they "hold" or wait for the inspection to be completed.
LTA	Less Than Adequate
MOC	Management of Change
NI	Needs Improvement
PIO	Potential Improvement Opportunity
PM	Preventive or Predictive Maintenance
QC	Quality Control
QV	Quality Verification
RBI	Risk Based Inspection
RCM	Reliability Centered Maintenance
SPAC	Standards, Policies, or Administrative Controls
Specs	Specifications
Typo	Typographical Error